A JOURNEY OF HOPE

Mike Arneson with recreational therapist Lora Harvey.

A Journey of Hope
Life Beyond Injury

Shepherd
Center

Written by John Yow

Photographs by Billy Howard

SHOCK DESIGN BOOKS

A division of Shock Design & Associates, Inc.
454 Hamilton Street, SE, #12, Atlanta, GA 30316
www.shockdesign.com

Sincere thanks go to Perry Ann Williams and Scott H. Sikes for their relentless and exhaustive efforts as book development coordinators at Shepherd Center.

Text copyright ©2010 John Yow

Book development, design, and production: Laurie Shock
Editor: Amy Bauman

First Edition

ISBN: 978-0-9824779-1-5
Library of Congress Control Number: 2010933592
Printed in China

Photo above: Jose Hernandez, patient.

Additional photo credits:
Pages viii–xv Shepherd family archives
Photo on page 122 © Gary Meek
Photo on page 139 © Thomas Elliott

TABLE OF CONTENTS

PREFACE

This is the story that began on October 21, 1973 at the top of a 14-foot wave, nearly ended at the bottom of the ocean and in so many ways, after 35 years, is still just beginning. I lived through 5 weeks in Brazil, paralyzed from the neck down and on a ventilator. Thanks to the care provided by Dr. Roberto Bibas, Dr. Aloysio Fonseca, Dr. Rue Kux, and the concern and help of Adolpho Gentil, I survived. Mother, Dad, Sherman Olsen, Frank Carter, Tommy Shepherd and God stayed with me in shifts 24 hours a day. There were times I thought my father would kill the doctors if I died. Mother would have beaten him to it but she never said so aloud.

I got out of Brazil thanks to Bill Renny of the U.S. Embassy who made the red tape vanish. Senator Herman Talmadge personally persuaded the Air Force to requisition a C-141 to fly me home to Atlanta at our expense. Once at Piedmont Hospital, I fought ten weeks for my survival under the care of Dr. Carter Smith, Jr., Dr. Newton Turk, several orthopedists, Peggy St. John RN and Frances Johnson RN. Every day my parents, my brother Tommy and my sister Dana could be found in the room tagging in and out. They helped suction me, scratch my head, wet my mouth with ice, or simply sat and prayed.

On February 5, 1974 we flew to Denver, CO. I weighed 82 pounds and was ready for rehabilitation. It was in the mountains of Denver on a 3-wheeler and still wearing a hard cervical collar that I discovered I could still enjoy life again even with physical deficits. I returned home on June 14, 1974 walking with a leg brace and a crutch. I invited Clark Harrison to lunch because I wanted to thank him for his weekly visits at Piedmont Hospital where he related his story of a successful life in a wheelchair and convinced me that my life was not over. He ran his own real estate company and had been elected to the DeKalb County Commission. I told Clark that someone should do spinal cord injury rehabilitation in Atlanta. That night I shared that thought with my parents. We kept bringing up the idea in our conversations and after a short period the dream began to take wings. The question was "who would do it and would we be a part of it?" The dream has been driven by the vision, values and hope of the Shepherd family. Dr. Dave Apple, Clark Harrison, David Webb, Roy Day and a small board of believing friends joined us between the Summer of 1974 and August 1975 to pursue the dream of doing spinal cord rehabilitation in Atlanta. Dave Webb and Clark Harrison were role models who had done rehabilitation on their own and knew no barriers.

These 35 years have seen Shepherd Center grow from a dream and 6 beds to a 132-bed facility serving spinal cord injuries, brain injuries, Multiple Sclerosis and chronic pain. The growth has been fueled by a team of dedicated and passionate staff, a tireless board of directors and a generous community.

Shepherd Center is patient- and family-centered with a laser-sharp focus on clinical excellence that incorporates re-engagement with life, leisure, families and work. We seek to have

our patients and families join us in seeing beyond their injury and embracing the exciting possibilities that exist for them. Shepherd Center today is far more than a rehabilitation hospital for spinal injuries, brain injuries, Multiple Sclerosis and chronic pain. We are a continuum of care wrapped around the patient and family beginning the day they are admitted to our ICU or our rehabilitation floors and extending beyond the day they leave. The family's stay begins in our housing so that they are engaged and educated side-by-side with the patient. The functional goals for the patient are far better when the family is a part of the team that includes our chaplains and therapeutic recreation.

We are a continuum of care wrapped around the patient and family beginning the day they are admitted.

What follows is our history including some of the marvelous miracles that all of us engaged with Shepherd Center, have had the privilege to witness and be a part of. I hope you are inspired by these stories as much as we have been.

Thanks for the role you play in making Shepherd Center a place of hope and where life begins again.

— James Shepherd
2010

INTRODUCTION
JAMES SHEPHERD AND SHEPHERD CENTER

THIRTY-SIX YEARS AGO, THE TELE-PHONE RANG in a northside Atlanta home on an otherwise peaceful Sunday morning. "It was ten o'clock, October 21, 1973," remembers Harold Shepherd. "Frank Carter was on the line, and there wasn't any reason for Frank to be on the line unless there was something bad wrong." Harold and Alana's son, James, had been traveling the world with two buddies, Frank Carter and Sherman Olsen, after their college graduation. "Egypt, Ethiopia, South Africa, and then to South America," says Harold, "where we had an interest in a ranch in Paraguay. That was going to be their last stop before coming home."

The boys didn't get to the ranch. When Harold got Frank's call, he wished he had heeded an earlier premonition. "It

James Shepherd embarking on his trip around the world.

was real strange," he says. "We had been to Brazil before for a trade association meeting, and my bag got misplaced. Those things happen, but for some reason the incident gave me a bad feeling about Rio. I said to Alana, 'This is just not a good place.' She said I was just upset because I had lost my bag, but I told her, 'There's something else.'"

Sure enough, the call came from Rio de Janeiro. The boys had been on the beach, body-surfing, when a wave caught James and smashed him against the ocean floor. His neck was broken. A lifeguard saw him tumbling around in the shallow surf and pulled him out, and then walked away, assuming James was either already dead or soon to be. Frank and Sherman saw the crowd gathering and ran over, and Sherman brought James back to consciousness with mouth-to-mouth resuscitation.

On Sunday morning in Atlanta, the banks were closed, and in 1973 the ATM had yet to make its appearance. Harold called everybody he knew, managed to gather a few thousand dol-

Casa de Saúde Sãn Miguel, the hospital that first treated James in Rio de Janeiro, Brazil.

lars, and then he and Alana sped to the airport. They were in Rio early Monday morning, where they were met at the airport by Adolfo Gentil, a friend and business associate of Harold's brother Clyde. "I had met him once before," says Harold. "Alana and I had been in Rio back in February, and he took the two of us and Clyde out to dinner. I called him after I got the news about James, and he was there to meet us. Also there to meet us was Atlanta friend Joe Hatch, who was working with Charles West's company."

Meanwhile, James's first 24 hours post injury were not easy. "I remember drowning and I remember waking up under a tin roof on the beach lying on a cot waiting for an ambulance. I went away again and woke up in an operating room under the care of a doctor I came to call . . . well, I don't need to repeat what I came to call him." James remembers that when he came to, the surgeon was shaving his head with a straight razor, and that he then began to insert the screws into each side of James's head for the tongs to put him in traction and, hopefully, reduce the fracture. "He was not a warm person," recalls James. "He kept screaming, 'Hold still!' And of course I was not cooperating." The problem was that there wasn't enough weight on the device to get the vertebrae back in alignment, so the doctor kept adding weight until the contraption tore loose from the side of James's head. "He didn't even wince," says James. "Just got a torque wrench and tightened the screws back in, telling me the whole time that it didn't really hurt. I'm fully conscious during the entire process."

To make matters worse, James's paralysis was not his only problem. He had also swallowed a lot of water, from a beach where sewage pipes run straight into the ocean, so he had developed pseudomonas and pneumonia. As Harold explains, "Their attitude at the hospital was, if you break your neck, you're never going to have any quality of life anyway, so they don't administer antibiotics. You get pneumonia and die." Harold called Adolfo Gentil, who then joined them at the hospital. "Adolfo and the doctor really got into it," says Harold, "but James started getting those antibiotics."

During five weeks in Brazil, James's condition remained critical, but the quality of his care improved dramatically with the arrival on the scene of Dr. Aloysio DeSalles Fonseca. James gives his friend Sherman all the credit here. "Sherman was really determined and resourceful," he says. "He called the American consulate, and they gave him the runaround, but he wouldn't have it. He insisted on getting in touch with the physician who takes care of the people there at the consulate." That man was Dr. Fonseca, and after Dr. Fonseca took the case, he was never far from James's bedside. "Even his wife became an advocate," says Harold. "We had dinner with them one night, and she told me, 'If you need to find him, call me. I always know where he is.'"

Working under Fonseca, who had been president of the South American Medical Association, was Dr. Roberto Bibas, a top-notch thoracic specialist. "He was an Egyptian-Brazilian-Jew," says Harold, "and we were very fortunate that he happened to be in Brazil rather than in Egypt or Israel." It was his responsibility to keep the pneumonia from killing James, to get him on a ventilator and deal with all the respiratory issues. "He was just a super guy," recalls James, "with a great bedside manner, great personality. He was completely engaged and interested. His attitude was, 'OK, we're not going to give up on this kid. I'll go to the ends of the earth if necessary.'"

And there were others whose kindness and generosity helped sustain the family during the crisis. Harold fondly remembers the Orburg brothers, who unexpectedly showed up at the hospital one day asking, "What do you need? What can we do?" They owned the Caterpillar dealership in Rio, so Harold can only assume that his good friend Goodloe Yancey, owner of Yancey Bros., the Caterpillar dealership in Atlanta, must have called Caterpillar headquarters in Peoria and had them call the dealership in Rio. The Orburgs, says Harold, were a couple of Brazilians who had gone to the University of Michigan, married American girls, then returned home to run Caterpillar in Rio. "They were amazing. They just busted their tails for us."

Then, when at last the time came to get James back home to Atlanta, there was Col. Bill Renny at the American consulate. "I had made a thousand trips to the consulate," recalls Harold, "talking to this person and that person about how to make the arrangements—and getting nowhere. Finally I complained to Adolfo, who asked me whom I'd been talking to. I told him, and he said, 'Wrong people. I'll make you an appointment.' On my next trip, I told the receptionist I wanted to see Col. Bill Renny. She stiffened visibly. Apparently nobody got to see Bill Renny. 'Do you have an appointment?' she sniffed. I told her I did, and she directed me to Renny's third-floor office. Bill Renny told me, 'You're a friend of Adolfo's, so you're a friend of mine. Here's every telephone number I've got—nights, weekends. Whatever I can do, just call me.'"

The following Sunday morning Harold's brother Dan called to say that the arrangements had been made, that an Air Force Medevac plane was standing by to come down and pick James up. All Harold had to do, Dan said, was get diplomatic clearance. "What do you mean I've got to get it?" Harold hollered. "I'm down here in a foreign country." Dan insisted that that's where it had to happen, so Harold called up the consul, General Lisset. "Aren't you a friend of Bill Renny's?" the general asked Harold, and when Harold said he hoped he was, Lisset said, "Well, call Bill." An hour and a half later, says Harold, they had the necessary clearance.

Actually, getting the clearance was not quite all Harold had to do. He also had to write a check

Shepherd family friend, Dr. Aolfo Gentil, in Rio de Janeiro, Brazil

for $32,000 to the U.S. Treasury, which eventually produced a pretty good story in its own right. "We had long been supporters of Herman Talmadge," recalls Harold, "and when he got into trouble with the Senate Ethics Committee, I realized that the Medevac trip from Rio to Atlanta might get looked into. So, just in case, I asked our CFO to get the cancelled check out of storage. Sure enough, a few months later our receptionist called my office to say that two men from the Senate Ethics Committee wanted to see me. When they got to my office, the first thing I did was ask to see their IDs. They showed them to me, and then it was their turn: 'We understand you had a free medical trip from Rio to Atlanta.' I asked them who told them that, and they said they couldn't tell me.

"I took the check out of my drawer and put it on my desk, along with copies, front and back. I told them they were welcome to the copies but not to touch the check. They examined their copies, and, noting that the check was made payable to the Secretary of the Treasury of the United States, one of them asked me who the secretary was. I told them that wasn't any concern of mine, that I had made out the check as requested. Then I asked the one who had asked me the question, 'Who is the Secretary of the Treasury now?' He had no idea.

Then one of them asked me if I had ever given Senator Talmadge any money. I said, 'Sure, several times.' 'When?' they asked. I told them I contributed to his campaign every time he ran for office, and, with that, I told them to get the hell out of my office."

Back in Rio, though, it was ultimately Aldofo Gentil who made everything happen. It was Gentil who was there to meet Harold and Alana at the airport, and from day one, it was Gentil who made sure that what needed to be done got done. At first the hospital insisted that Harold pay cash—in American dollars—for all of James's medical expenses, adding an extra, and unnecessary, ton to the weight of the family's burden. It was Gentil who took Harold down to the bank and "persuaded" them to open an account "He handed the clerk two letters," recalls Harold. "He said, 'The first one is from the guy who owns this bank, and the second one is from me. You open an account for Mr. Shepherd, right now, and if the charges get over a million dollars you let me know, and I'll take care of it.'"

Of course, if it hadn't been for Gentil's intercession, there would have been no diplomatic clearance via Col. Renny. And even that's not the end of the story. With the clearance established, Harold got a call from the Air Force colonel. There was a problem with the radar, he said. It would probably be two or three days before he could get it fixed. James didn't have that kind of time. Harold called Adolfo, whose secretary had formerly worked for Varig Airlines in South America. The radar problem was solved within two hours. As James puts it, "Everything goes back to Adolfo. He was one of those people who could make things happen with a phone call."

All these years later, Harold can laugh over a family anecdote. When James's sister, Dana, got married, Adolfo came up for the wedding but wasn't content to play the role of the typical guest. "He wanted to do like they do in Brazil and walk down the aisle behind the bride," says Harold. "I had to tell him, 'Adolfo, we don't do that up here. You just come sit with the family.' Then Harold returns to the point: "If not for Adolfo, James is not here today. No question."

Even with Adolfo, James figures he got out of Brazil just in time. He was there for five weeks and doubts that he could have held on another two. No wonder—massive antibiotics, no food, and, in one two-day period, 22 units of blood due to stress ulcers. "Mother says they found 17 ulcers in my stomach," he says, "bleeding so profusely that they could hear it with a stethoscope."

At the end of November, the Air Force jet finally waited on the tarmac. If the long-awaited departure was a huge relief for Harold and Alana, for James it was a very weird trip. Sedated with some kind of experimental drug that had never been approved in the United States, he spent the next two days in and out of a hallucinatory fever-dream, imagining at one point that he was not on a plane at all but on a pirate ship in a mossy lagoon somewhere near New Orleans. "It was as real as this room," James says in his office today.

Once the plane touched down at Dobbins Air Force Base in Marietta, James was transported to Piedmont Hospital, where, the family fervently hoped, everything would be fine. But Piedmont was not a spinal cord rehabilitation hospital, and after more than two months there, James was no better. He wasn't dead, though, and for that he gives the hospital due credit. "No question, they did a great job of keeping me alive—through a couple of cardiac arrests, respiratory failures, acute fevers of 105 and 106. They did everything they knew how to do."

Harold concurs, and he remembers with eternal gratitude the compassion and dedication of the nurses who helped keep James going. There was Frances Johnson, for example, who conspired with Harold to get James some longed-for fresh air, even though the means were not exactly orthodox. "It was a beautiful winter morning—probably 60 degrees outside—and I went into James's room and said, 'Get hold of the bed, Johnson. We're taking him outside.' We rolled James right out through the lobby of the hospital, with Frances managing to keep the IVs and everything connected. I thought the administrator was going to have a stroke, but Frances and I were determined to get him out of that hospital room and into the sunlight and fresh air."

Another was Peggy St. John, whose vivacious personality impressed Harold the first time they met. Thinking James was asleep, Harold entered his room quietly, and Peggy, who was examining a bottle in the light from the window, was startled to suddenly hear his voice. "She dropped the bottle and hollered 'Oh [expletive deleted]!,'" remembers Harold, "and I knew right then we would get along fine." Seriously, though, Peggy really earned her stripes "during those terrible days right after they took James off the ventilator." He could swallow but couldn't keep food down, and he was already dangerously emaciated. Harold told Peggy, "St. John, you've got to figure something out. He'll die if he can't eat." Peggy went out and got a can of Ensure, then told Harold to go home and blend it up into a milkshake with a couple of eggs and a few scoops of ice cream. "When I got back with the milkshake, she was waiting there with a bladder irrigator. 'His bladder's not the problem,' I told her, and she told me she was going to put the milkshake in the bladder irrigator, hang it up on the IV pole, hook the bladder irrigator to the nose tube and drip that milkshake into him one drop at a time. Pretty soon James was taking in 1,200 calories a day."

But keeping James alive was one thing. Recuperation was another. "Piedmont had no clue what to do from a rehab standpoint," says James. He had no muscle strength, no cardiac strength; he was skin and skeleton. "Their prognosis was that I would remain paralyzed, never get out of bed, and basically my life would be miserable. They actually held out DNR—"do not resuscitate"—as an option. It was really the same outlook they had in Brazil."

The family had watched long enough. Harold and Spencer Smith, Alana's brother, flew to Denver to check out Craig Hospital, the well-known rehabilitation facility. They flew back that night, and Harold told James what he had seen there. "What do you want to do?" he asked.

"Let's go," said James.

Harold remembers telling the doctor in charge that day to get James ready, that they were leaving, and that the doctor had tried to object. As Harold puts it today, "Frankly, I wasn't much fun to be around at that point in my life, and I'm afraid I told that doctor in no uncertain terms that he didn't need to be telling me what I could and could not do."

At Harold's request, Dan called Rankin Smith, then the owner of the Atlanta Falcons, to see if they could rent his plane for a couple of days. According to Harold's version, Smith asked Dan why he wanted the plane, and when Dan told him, Smith said, "No, you can't rent it, but we'll be happy to take James to Denver." Harold tried to protest, telling Smith that he couldn't fly his Gulfstream I from Atlanta to Denver and back for nothing. When he begged Smith to at least let him pay for the fuel, Smith told him, "Harold, you call me again, and you don't get the plane." Harold says Smith refused to take the first penny. "And he got pretty tired of me thanking him, too." Few people ever knew Rankin Smith was responsible for getting James to Denver, says Harold, which was the way Smith liked it. "He was a private person, and he did a lot of things for other people that nobody knew about."

James spent four and a half months at Craig. "A long time," says Harold, "because he had

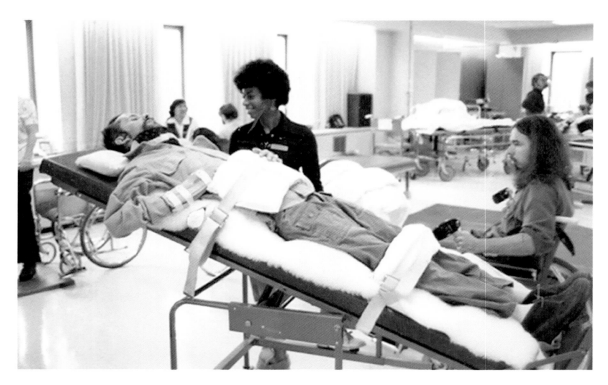

James Shepherd at Craig Hospital in Denver, Colorado in 1974.

gone so far downhill." But everybody knew at once that he had finally come to the right place.

"Their whole idea," says James, "was 'Let's get up, let's get out of bed, let's go to work.' And they knew how to do it."

On Friday, June 13, 1974, James walked out of the hospital with a leg brace and a crutch.

"How Can We Do It Better?"

James's recovery wasn't a miracle. It was a matter of a determined patient at last getting inside the doors of an excellent rehabilitation facility. In the 35 years since James walked out of Craig, thousands of spinal cord-injured patients have received world-class rehabilitation at Atlanta's own Shepherd Center. That's not a miracle either. But it's quite a story. In a nutshell, it goes like this: At the beginning, a handful of people asked themselves, "What can we do?" And in all the years since, an ever-expanding group of people have kept asking themselves, "How can we do it better?"

As it turned out, James was not the only Atlantan who had had to go to the other side of the United States for spinal cord rehabilitation. There was former DeKalb County commission chairman Clark Harrison, who first told James about Craig Hospital. There was Roy Day Jr., who had told Harrison about Craig. Back in Atlanta, James and Clark and Roy found themselves agreeing that Denver was too far to have to go, that such a facility in Atlanta would serve people all over the Southeast. (It was a big idea, but not as big as the subsequent reality. As it enters its 35th year, Shepherd has served patients from all 50 states and from more than three dozen foreign countries.)

What can we do? Well, Harold and Alana could get on the telephone and knock on doors, calling on everybody from big-name foundations to small-town garden clubs. James and Clark

James, Harold and Alana Shepherd.

Harrison could educate the donor community on the nature of spinal cord injury and the demand for a facility in the Southeast. Atlanta orthopedist Dr. David Apple could throw over the security of his established practice and "go all in" as the new facility's medical director. He could also scout around and locate some space in an empty wing of a northwest Atlanta hospital.

So the initial question was speedily answered. On August 19, 1975, one short, hectic year after the idea was conceived, Shepherd Spinal Center opened its doors. It didn't seem like much—two doctors (including orthopedist Herndon Murray, whom Dr. Apple had somehow convinced to jump on board), three therapists, nurse support from the leasing hospital, and enough space to accommodate six patients—but it was a beginning . . . and there was no turning back.

By the end of its second year of operation, the center had treated more than 200 patients for spinal cord injury. Then the thing really exploded: the third year doubled the number of total admissions, to 417; by the end of year four, Shepherd had 60 full-time employees; and new programs, like outpatient care and recreational therapy, were providing initial answers to that second, always-pressing question, "How can we do it better?"

An even better answer came thanks to Atlanta real estate developer Scott Hudgens. Not long after James's accident, Hudgens, too, had had a family tragedy and called Harold because a friend of Harold's worked for Scott. Harold and Hudgens talked frequently during those days, and, as Harold says, "I think maybe I helped Scott get through it." Fast forward to 1980, when Shepherd Center was five years old and thinking that it might be wise to move next door to Piedmont Hospital. By sheer good luck, Hudgens owned four and a half acres next to Piedmont that was being used for a parking lot.

Harold called Hudgens and asked if the land was for sale. "Scott said, 'What are you going to do with it?'" recalls Harold. "I told him the land wasn't for me but for Shepherd Spinal Center. He paused and said, 'That's different. I'll get back to you in a couple of days.'" Harold remembers telling Jim Caswell, a long-time friend and Shepherd board member, what he was trying to do, and Caswell's response was, "Scott Hudgens is the smartest land man that ever lived."

True to form, Hudgens called a few days later and said, "Here is the deal. The property is worth $1,300,000. I have offered it to Piedmont Hospital for $1,500,000. I will sell it to Shepherd Center for $1,000,000, and the day you buy it, I will give Shepherd a check for $200,000." As Harold puts it today, "Sure enough, an appraiser came in and confirmed Scott's estimate of the property's worth. Now I'm not a rocket scientist, but I believe we got a discount of $500,000."

One of Shepherd's board members insisted that the checks be swapped at the closing, says Harold. "As instructed, our lawyer asked Scott where the check for $200,000 was. Scott replied that he didn't know where it was, and when the lawyer pressed him, he said, 'I gave it to James 30 minutes ago, and I have no idea what James did with it.' Of course, Scott was just jerking the lawyer's chain."

For Harold, the whole episode was just more evidence that "this was all meant to be." And so it was that in October 1980, just a few weeks after the center's fifth birthday, ceremonial shovels broke ground at the site. Eighteen months—and $8 million—later, an exultant ribbon-cutting opened the doors of Shepherd Spinal Center's gleaming new 93,000-square-foot facility at 2020 Peachtree Road. James recalls watching the tears of joy stream down the face of founding board member Dave Webb as he cut the ribbon. For Dr. Apple, "It was pure liberation."

In addition to a new building that year, Shepherd Spinal Center also got a $246,000 grant from the U.S. Department of Education's Rehabilitation Services Administration. But it wasn't just the money, nor the fact that of 50 applicants, Shepherd was one of only 17 award-winners. The real significance of the award was that it meant official designation of the center as one of the country's elite "model programs" in spinal injury rehabilitation—a designation it has continued to enjoy ever since. After a scant seven years in operation, it was an eye-popping accolade.

The new space allowed for the growth of the kinds of programs that were becoming Shepherd's hallmark—peer support, vocational services, the outdoor program, advocacy—programs that looked beyond injury rehabilitation and toward full reintegration into the community. "How can we do it better?" Here's Alana's answer: "We want our patients to be able to return to doing whatever they enjoyed doing before they were injured, even if they have to do it differently."

Mark Johnson, Director of Advocacy program at Shepherd.

At age 12, the center first published its annual report, in the Fall 1987 issue of its *Spinal Column* magazine. The report noted among its highlights that Shepherd was now the "nation's largest facility specializing exclusively in spinal cord disorders"; that it was one of only 13 U.S. hospitals federally designated as "models of care"; and that it served patients from 20 states that year, as well as from three foreign countries. The report also pointed to one of the reasons for Shepherd's phenomenal success: while the ratio of patients to staff in the typical nonspecialized hospital was three to one, the ratio at Shepherd was four staff members to each patient.

Ten years after the move to Peachtree Road, the center doubled in size again—with a $23 million, 153,000-square-feet expansion. At the dedication of the new Billi Marcus Building, U.S. Senator Max Cleland called Shepherd "the finest rehabilitation center for spinal cord injury in the nation." It would soon become much more.

The Marcus Building provided expansive quarters for Shepherd's newly created MS Center, which immediately was designated by the National Multiple Sclerosis Society as the only comprehensive center of its type in the Southeast. Then, with the 1994 hiring of Dr. Gary Ulicny, Ph.D., as the center's first president and CEO, Shepherd moved into a third area of specialty—acquired brain injury (ABI). The rationale was indisputable: first, there was no comprehensive facility in the Southeast dedicated to the treatment of brain injury; and, second, a significant number of patients arriving at the hospital with spine injury also had brain injury. As Ulicny put it, "This move solidifies Shepherd's position as a center of excellence in the treatment of catastrophic injury." A name change the following year—to Shepherd Center, a Catastrophic Care Hospital—reflected its enhanced status.

Ten years after the move to Peachtree Road, Shepherd Center doubled in size again—with a $23 million, 153,000-square-foot expansion. At the dedication of the new Bill Marcus Building, U.S. Senator Max Cleland called Shepherd "the finest rehabilitation center for spinal cord injury in the nation."

"How can we do it better?" By 1997 the ABI unit had already established its remarkable off-campus outpatient program, Shepherd Pathways, to better manage the full recovery of patients with brain injury. It was a strategic move into "community-based outpatient services," and yet more evidence of Shepherd's commitment to the "full continuum" of rehabilitation services. At the same time, the National Institute on Disability and Rehabilitation Research designated Shepherd as a "model center" for the treatment of brain injury as well as spinal injury. According to Dr. Donald Leslie, the original director of the ABI program. "The fact that after only two years we were selected as a model brain injury program is a great tribute to what we've accomplished. And we are one of the very few—a very small handful—of hospitals in the country that have model programs in both spinal cord injury and brain injury."

Shepherd's efforts to set itself apart from other hospitals in terms of its "continuum of care" were magnificently abetted by a $17.6 million grant from the Marcus Foundation to establish the Marcus Community Bridge Program—expressly intended to provide up to 12 months of follow-up care to every "at-risk" patient who comes through the doors of Shepherd Center. The grant would allow Shepherd to develop the best possible transition-to-home services for departing patients—including telemedicine technology, vocational services, self-care education, and therapeutic recreation in clients' own communities. Tammy King, the program's director, called it "the perfect extension of Shepherd's whole effort. We never stop asking, 'How can we make it better.'"

When it turned 25 in the year 2000, Shepherd Center had grown from a six-bed unit serving people with spinal cord injuries to an innovator in acute catastrophic care, rehabilitation, and research; the premiere spinal cord injury facility in the country; the largest brain injury rehabilitation program in the state of Georgia; and the largest Multiple Sclerosis Center in the nation. Not about to slow down, it burst into the new century with the announcement of a $60 million capital and endowment campaign that would increase endowment from $8 million to $38 million over four years; expand medical services, research, and follow-up support to patients as they return to the community; and revitalize the Shepherd campus.

With the new century's first decade scarcely half over, the fruit of the campaign was ripening spectacularly—epitomized by the opening of the Jane Woodruff Pavilion (a 170,000-square-foot, multistory addition to the Marcus Building) and the Irene and George Woodruff Family Residence Center. Standing next door on the site of an old hotel that had been purchased and demolished, the $17 million residence center dramatically exemplifies Shepherd's determination to "do it better." Funded entirely by donor contributions (including a significant amount from Shepherd employees), the residence center's 84 wheelchair-accessible suites make it possible for families to be not only close by but also intimately involved in their loved ones' rehabilitation—a universally acknowledged benefit to the recovery effort.

The quest continues. The Spinal Cord Injury (SCI) department has moved "Beyond Therapy" with a new program that recognizes patients' need to continue to receive intense therapy beyond that provided by traditional healthcare. By working to maximize muscle return, it helps people with spinal cord injury improve their lifelong health, minimize secondary complications and get the most out of any new neural links to their muscles. The ABI program—again thanks to the generosity of Bernie Marcus—is now reaching out to veterans of the wars in Iraq and Afghanistan with its Shaping Hope and Recovery Excellence (SHARE) initiative, offering state-of-the-art rehabilitation to military personnel who have suffered brain injury. And in the ongoing search for that elusive cure for multiple sclerosis, Shepherd's MS Center is one of six U.S. sites involved in a national data collection study spearheaded by Accelerated Cure Project for Multiple Sclerosis, a national nonprofit investigating the cause of the disease.

No wonder, then, that for the past two years, 2008 and 2009, after climbing steadily up the rankings for a decade, Shepherd Center now ranks in the "Top 10"—named the nation's ninth-best rehabilitation hospital by U.S. *News & World Report* in its annual list of "America's Best Hospitals." Shepherd CEO Dr. Gary Ulicny was justifiably pleased: "We are honored to rank among the top rehabilitation hospitals in the country and especially proud to be the highest ranked rehabilitation hospital in the Southeast. Being included for the tenth year in a row shows that our peers are recognizing the specialty care we offer to individuals who've experienced a catastrophic injury or illness."

True enough. But how about this unbiased assessment from "Best Hospital" editor Avery Comarow: "Talent and money alone don't put hospitals in the rankings. The truly best hospitals are never satisfied. Of course they have high medical standards. But the emphasis is not only on doing well but always doing better."

At Shepherd, that's been the idea for 35 years.

Opposite page, left to right: James, Alana, and Harold Shepherd.

THE SPINAL CORD INJURY PROGRAM

Shepherd Center started its journey as a spinal cord injury rehabilitation hospital, and, make no mistake, it still is a spinal cord injury rehabilitation hospital—one of the best in the world. To be sure, its scope and mission have expanded, accurately reflected in its 1995 change of name to Shepherd Center—A Catastrophic Care Hospital. But its history in spinal cord injury rehabilitation is distinguished, and its future is limitless.

Many of the SCI programs, research efforts, and personnel will be highlighted in the pages that follow. For this preliminary overview, let's begin with the facts and figures.

From six in 1975, the number of patient beds in the SCI unit has grown to 120, and Shepherd is now licensed for 132.

For the most recent full year (2008), 374 patients were admitted to the inpatient program; 263 participated in the Day Program; and 630 took advantage of the "outpatient continuum."

Shepherd is the only center in the United States that offers a full continuum of care to people with spinal cord injury—consisting of:

· A 10-bed ICU.
· An acute rehabilitation program (the largest, most comprehensive in the nation), with dedicated programs for patients with high tetraplegia; adolescents (ages 12–18); young adults (ages 19–49); older adults (ages 50 and older); and dual diagnosis patients (i.e., patients with spinal cord injury and brain injury).
· A spinal cord injury Day Program, which bridges the need for care between inpatient hospitalization and maximal independent living at home.
· Outpatient/Therapy programs, for patients who don't need a comprehensive program but who can benefit from one or more of those available—physical therapy, occupational therapy, speech therapy, counseling, or case management.
· Beyond Therapy, an intense activity-based health and wellness program.

Physical therapist Jennifer Smith with patient Anthony Puckett.

Shepherd Center became the first in the nation to offer a diaphragm pacing system (DPS) program under new Food and Drug Administration (FDA) regulations set forth in May 2008.

Shepherd was one of only seven hospitals in the nation selected by the Christopher and Dana Reeve Foundation to participate in its groundbreaking NeuroRecovery Network research project.

The stats and data are courtesy of Sarah Morrison, director of the SCI program. "And don't forget," says Morrison, "that Shepherd remains one of the country's elite 'model programs' in spinal care injury rehabilitation." As an indication of how tough it is to achieve that designation, when Shepherd was first named, there were 17 such centers; now there are 14.

In her 25 years at Shepherd, Morrison has had a pretty good look at the growth and evolution of the spinal cord injury unit. One of the most interesting changes she has documented is the steady increase in the numbers of incomplete injuries—and how that has shaped program development. "More than half of our patients now are incomplete," she says, "and therefore have a higher potential for a return to walking." That explains why Shepherd is probably the only rehab hospital in the country to have two robotic treadmill centers ("Most facilities don't even have one"), not to mention three state-of-the-art therapy-assisted treadmill systems. There is also the impressive array of high-tech electrical stimulation equipment, all of which, says Morrison, "provide us the opportunity to help more and more people get back to walking. This is an area where we have really kept ahead of the curve, in terms of our programming."

Morrison has also kept a hawk's eye on another steady trend over the years: the constant pressure from insurance companies to shorten the average length of stay for patients in rehab. Here are the telling stats, broken down into (1) acute stage length of stay and (2) rehab stage length of stay: In 1974, the acute stage stay lasted an average of 25 days; in 2004, it was down to 15 days. In 1974, the rehab stage averaged 115 days; in 2004, 36 days.

"But," says Morrison, "that's what our continuum of care is all about. That's why we developed our Day Program." Those numbers tell a story, too. A report from the year 2000 documents 85 people in the Day Program. For the most recent year, that number had swelled to 263. "So that program has really kicked in as length of stay has shrunk. Because people want to finish their rehab, which they should." That's the kind of thinking that keeps Morrison motivated: "getting those patients and families back to having a good quality of life again. Whatever potential for recovery is there, our job is to exploit it to the fullest."

Needless to say, Morrison has also been around to witness the spectacular expansion of the physical plant. Hired on when the Shepherd Building on Peachtree was still a recent marvel, she has been delighted to see the center double in size and then double again, with the renovation of the Billi Marcus Building and the addition of the new Jane Woodruff Pavilion. "The new space has been wonderful," says Morrison. "It not only houses our day programs and outpatient program but also ancillary services like assistive technology and the seating clinic, which also serve us." Morrison points out, too, that since the Magnetic Resonance Imaging (MRI) center was moved into the Woodruff Pavilion, "our Beyond Therapy and ProMotion facilities now have twice as much space." Best of all, once the fifth floor of the Pavilion was finished in late 2009, "it provided 35 new private rooms for the spinal cord unit."

Medical director emeritus Dr. David F. Apple shares the excitement. "It's pretty

William Henry Hardee, of Lavonia GA, uses one of the manual treadmills.

spectacular," he says of the new addition. "To have space to grow into is a wonderful luxury." He also agrees with Morrison that Shepherd's programs are what "make us unique." He cites the Marcus Community Bridge Program, Beyond Therapy, the SHARE Initiative as among "the newer ones—evidence that we never stop finding better ways to fulfill our mission." But as he looks back, Dr. Apple has no trouble identifying the program that "really set us apart": therapeutic recreation. "Before Shepherd came along," he explains, "every SCI program had a recreational therapist, but none had a recreational therapy department. That program really demonstrated our mission: to show people that they could fish, hunt, bowl, whatever—and that from there they could return to life, to a good quality of life. That's the idea that generated all the other programs: the idea that we want our patients to fully participate in life." What Dr. Apple doesn't mention is that his commitment to recreational therapy was such that he paid the salary of the first recreational therapist out of his own pocket.

Shepherd's successful patient programs are closely bound up with the SCI unit's far-reaching research efforts, which also, Dr. Apple points out, "are always working to improve our patients' lives." There's no telling what might lie ahead, "whether in terms of neuroplasticity, stem cell therapies, or who knows what." But Dr. Apple notes that Shepherd is by no means exclusively focused on the "miracle repair" of the broken spinal cord. "Imagine what it would mean to a spinal cord injured patient's quality of life to have his bowel and bladder function back," he says. "So it will continue to be critical to our mission to think in terms of these increments of improvement— improvements in the lives of the patients we have today."

Meanwhile, the hospital continues to grow, and so does its reputation, nationally and internationally. Dr. Donald Leslie, Dr. Apple's successor as medical director, who "came here as a resident in 1983 and never left," is particularly gratified to have witnessed Shepherd's steady rise in the eyes of the world. "The fact that we are now ranked among the nation's top ten rehab hospitals by U.S. News & World Report is really terrific, especially for a nonaffiliated hospital like

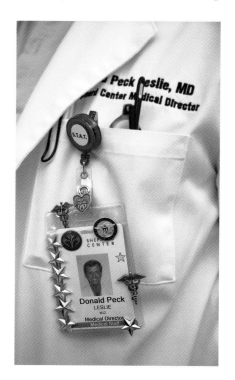

us." Though Shepherd is "intimately connected through collaborative research efforts" with highly regarded educational institutions like Emory University, Georgia Tech, the University of Georgia and the University of Florida, it's a point worth emphasizing that "we are ultimately free-standing, and, in fact, the largest free-standing rehab hospital in the nation, if not the world."

To illustrate Shepherd's stature on the world's stage, Dr. Leslie mentions that he and one of Shepherd's therapists traveled to New Delhi, India, to evaluate a young man who was injured in a car wreck there in the summer of 2008. His family wants him to come to the United States for rehab once he has recovered sufficiently to travel, so they have personally toured all of the best hospitals in the country—the Rehabilitation Institute of Chicago, Jackson Memorial Medical Center in Miami, Craig in Denver, The Institute for Rehabilitation and Research (TIRR) in Houston, and Mt. Sinai in New York, among

Dr. David Apple, Medical Director Emeritus.

VALEDICTORY

"It's been a wonderful journey, and a great career for me," says founding medical director Dr. David Apple, who formally passed the reins to his successor, Dr. Donald Peck Leslie, on April 1, 2005. "I suppose the most remarkable aspect of it all is these buildings that surround us here today. When I think about starting out with six beds in that now nonexistent hospital on Howell Mill Road and see where we are now, just in terms of the physical space we've created, it's really hard to believe."

It was Dr. Apple, you remember, who was somehow convinced to buy into the Shepherd family's far-fetched dream of a spinal cord injury rehab hospital in Atlanta. He was a young orthopedic surgeon at the time. His fourth child was on the way. Surely there were doubts, second thoughts. "No," Dr. Apple declares. "Absolutely not. There was never a question in my mind about what we were doing. In fact, though the Shepherds might not remember it this way, I may have been the one pushing the hardest.

Whether there have been any regrets since is an

Thank God for Dr. Apple. He allowed us to have some autonomy, and that made it fun, and interesting, and challenging. So many of us were inspired by his attitude. We couldn't help but get inspired.

— TAMMY KING

even easier question. "There was never time to look back, nor any reason to, because we were growing from day one. Every minute there was something else, something new, to preoccupy us. Every day brought a new challenge, and every day was exciting."

For the hospital's immediate and enduring success, Dr. Apple is quick to pass along the credit. "One of the truly remarkable things is that, whenever those new challenges did come up, there was always somebody in the community stepping forward to help us meet them—often thanks to Harold and Alana's wide circle of devoted friends. Like Scott Hudgens, who helped us acquire this property on Peachtree. Or like Virginia Crawford, or Billi and Bernie Marcus, or Jane Woodruff. I can't imagine where we would be without all these wonderful benefactors—and countless others." Dr. Apple also fondly recalls the contributions of early board members like John Aderhold and Goodloe Yancey. "And Sally Nunnally," he adds. "You know, it's a strange irony, but we got a tremendous boost in the community when Sally was injured and came to Shepherd. It seemed like everybody in Atlanta visited Sally while she was here—people who otherwise had no knowledge of spinal cord injury and no knowledge of us. It generated a lot of exposure that we hadn't had before. It was appropriate that she went on to serve on our board of directors."

Of course, Dr. Apple is equally appreciative of the people in the hospital, especially those early hires—doctors, therapists, nurses—who worked indefatigably to get the enterprise up and running, and who, in many cases, are still at Shepherd today. He's reluctant to start naming names, though, for fear of forgetting somebody. "You know who you are," he says instead.

At the same time, Dr. Apple concedes that his years at Shepherd have constituted a gratifying personal journey as well. To put it in perspective, he explains that he went to medical school, post-grad training, fellowships, etc., all the while thinking that he wanted to be an orthopedic surgeon. But after four or five years of being an orthopedic surgeon, he began rethinking. "Of course, being an orthopedic surgeon was fine; I was helping my patients, doing what I was supposed to do. But I couldn't help noticing that I was just one of probably several hundred orthopedic surgeons in Georgia alone. What could I do, I started to wonder, that would set me apart, that would make my career somehow different?"

That's exactly what the opportunity at Shepherd offered, he says—"A chance to start something, to see it grow, to think that maybe 40 or even 100 years from now Shepherd Center will still be here, still helping people. If I had finished out my career as an orthopedic surgeon, I would never have been a part of that kind of legacy. So to have helped create something that will endure, a legacy that I'm a part of, is really gratifying."

During his tenure at Shepherd, Dr. Apple has been the recipient of every imaginable accolade. He particularly cherishes having been named Humanitarian of the Year by the American Academy of Orthopedic Surgeons, as well as receiving the Vernon Nickel Award for his "many contributions" to the field—given in honor of the renowned head of Rancho Los Amigos, the famous rehab hospital in Los Angeles. "Vernon Nickel was one of my heroes," explains Dr. Apple. "I had a fellowship there, and it was Dr. Nickel who told us, 'Go out from here and do something to help others. Go out and make a difference.'"

In this brief retrospective, though, Dr. Apple would rather talk about great moments in the history of the hospital, and one of his favorites occurred in 1996, when Shepherd was instrumental in bringing the Paralympics to Atlanta along with the Olympic Games. When it hosted the Games in 1984, Los Angeles had refused to have anything to do with the Paralympics, Dr. Apple explains, and Shepherd was determined that that wouldn't happen again. "It wasn't easy. We had huge issues with the Atlanta Committee for the Olympic Games (ACOG)—to get them to see us as part of the event. But we persevered, and it was really exciting, very gratifying." He adds that it was also important for Shepherd Center, because the International Medical Society of Paraplegia had its 1996 annual conference at Shepherd, "so doctors from all over the world were walking up and down our hallways. I have to say that was one of our greatest accomplishments."

Dr. Apple remains active both in the hospital (where he's emeritus chief in the Crawford Research Center as well as attached to the foundation staff) and outside of it (where he has two different consulting jobs.) But what he likes to do, he says, "is hang around and try to help make sure that Shepherd continues to be such a fun place to work."

THIS LIST RECOGNIZES, WITH GRATITUDE, THOSE DEDICATED EMPLOYEES WHO HAVE BEEN WORKING AT SHEPHERD CENTER FOR 25 YEARS OR MORE:

Myrtice Atrice
THERAPY MANAGER

Sara ("Sally") Atwell
RESEARCH PROJECT COORDINATOR

Betsy Banan
BAYLOR RN

Jacquelyn Boone
INPATIENT RN

Ruth Fierman
OCCUPATIONAL THERAPIST

Jane Huckeba
ADVANCED BRIDGE BUILDER

Lesley Hudson
CLINICAL RESEARCH MANAGER

Tammy King
CHIEF NURSE EXECUTIVE

Nell ("Winnie") Klein
OUTPATIENT RN

Sarah Morrison
SCI PROGRAM DIRECTOR

Kathleen Slonaker
ADMISSIONS LIAISON

Marilyn Taylor
CASE MANAGER

Joanie Ventresca
THERAPY MANAGER

Amanda Wilcoxson
PURCHASING AGENT

Dr. Herndon Murray, Medical Director, Spinal Cord Injury Program.

others. "And they chose us," says Dr. Leslie. "We've tried not to hurt our arms patting ourselves on the back, but we're mighty pleased and proud that after seeing firsthand what all the other centers were like, they thought our program was the best. It's a nice vote of confidence."

There is another change. Of the four admitting physicians in the SCI unit, only one, Dr. Herndon Murray (now the medical director of the unit) is an orthopedic surgeon. As Dr. Leslie puts it, "This hospital was built by orthopedics—Drs. David Apple, Herndon Murray, Allen Mc-Donald—and when I came on as the physiatrist, the person with formal training in rehab, I was the odd man out. Now we've turned the tables around. Now Dr. Murray is by himself as the only orthopedic surgeon, and across the hospital we now have nine physiatrists. The result of that is good, in that physical medicine is the specialty of rehabilitation."

Dr. Murray doesn't argue the point; in fact, he agrees that the increasing number of physiatrists in the hospital is "part of the natural course of events." Putting those events in perspective, he explains that "back when we were starting out, there really weren't any physiatrists in Atlanta," and that, more generally "orthopedists took care of rehab before there was any real rehab specialty." Now rehabilitation has evolved into its own specialty, and it's appropriate that physiatrists are the designated specialists. But, says Dr. Murray, as he looks back over Shepherd's history, "I guess we orthopedic guys did okay."

LIVING IN THE NOW

_T_HOSE
2:00 A.M. PHONE CALLS
SELDOM BRING GOOD NEWS. The one that
shook a quiet bedroom in Fredericksburg, Virginia, on September 14, 2007,
was no exception.

Cheryl Hazel calls it the "never-in-your-wildest-dreams" phone call.
When her husband, Dick, answered it, he found himself talking to the emergency room nurse from the hospital on the campus of the University of the
South, in Sewanee, Tennessee, where the Hazels' daughter, Caroline, was
enrolled. "She wanted insurance information," says Dick. "She said our
daughter had been injured, and they were trying to MedEvac her to
Chattanooga." Dick got the information and also got a doctor on the
line. "But all he could tell us was that she could move her arms and had
some feeling in her legs."

The four years on that pretty mountaintop in Tennessee that
had loomed so pleasantly in Caroline Hazel's imagination suffered
a drastic and sudden disruption. "I was there for three weeks before
I got hurt," says Caroline. "I was on the fire escape balcony of a fraternity house, and somebody opened the door to come out. I
scooted aside to get out of the way, and the balcony rail gave way."
Caroline thinks she must have lost consciousness briefly, because she remembers falling but not hitting the ground. Coming to, the first thing she
was aware of was severe pain in her neck, but otherwise, she felt relief. "I
was like, 'Oh my gosh, I'm OK'—because I knew how far I had fallen. I
thought maybe I had broken a bone or two, but . . ."

Emergency Medical Services (EMS) volunteers rushed her to the
hospital on campus, where medical personnel quickly realized that Caroline
needed to be transported to Erlanger Hospital in
Chattanooga. When they got
hold of

Dick and Cheryl at 2:00 A.M., their idea was a helicopter airlift. But it was a rainy, foggy night on the mountain, so Caroline was driven down to the hospital via ambulance.

Meanwhile, Dick and Cheryl got on the first flight from Fredericksburg to Chattanooga, "without knowing," says Cheryl, "much at all about what the situation was." At the hospital they were met by the attending trauma physician, who could scarcely have greeted them with more disturbing news: "He told us that Caroline had suffered a catastrophic spinal cord injury," recalls Cheryl. "He said she will be a quadriplegic, that she would never walk, and that she might never use her arms again."

"He listed the different breaks she had," adds Dick. "C-5, L-2, ribs, scapula. Our ignorance of what these things signified was enormous, but we would learn that the C-5 was the critical injury."

The last person to learn the extent—and significance—of her injuries was Caroline herself. "I had no idea I was paralyzed," she says. "Nobody actually ever told me."

"It was a bad parenting moment," says Cheryl ruefully. "And difficult to understand in retrospect," adds Dick. But as their story makes clear, there was no bad parenting going on, and their failure to convey this information to Caroline is not so difficult to understand after all. In the first place, Caroline would have likely realized it—or at least suspected it—on her own, except that she was undergoing one major surgery after another and was "pretty much out of it" the whole time she was at Erlanger. Second, as Cheryl puts it, "I guess we were waiting for a doctor to take the lead in explaining the diagnosis to Caroline." Not an unreasonable expectation, but "that never happened."

> *The attending trauma physician told us that Caroline had suffered a catastrophic spinal cord injury. He said that she will be a quadriplegic, that she would never walk, and that she might never use her arms again.*
>
> —Cheryl Hazel

Finally, Dick and Cheryl were simply in uncharted waters. "We had no point of reference," says Cheryl. "We had not been there. The learning curve is steep, and there's no warm-up." Not to mention the fact that the two parents had left five other children at home. "It was just crazy," says Cheryl, "and we were caught up in the swirl."

On the other hand, they did realize they caught a break when what might have been Caroline's third operation, the repair of the shattered L-2, was accomplished as part of the second operation, allowing Caroline to be discharged from Erlanger several days earlier than would otherwise have been the case. But that gave rise to a new set of questions. "They started talking about referring her to a rehab hospital," recalls Dick, "but we were so in the dark, we had no idea what they were talking about."

"We were like, 'Time out!'" adds Cheryl.

As Dick recounts, their "angel" finally arrived in the person of a Dr. Paul Hoffman, a physiatrist affiliated with the rehab hospital next door to Erlanger, whose name had been given to them by a friend back in Fredericksburg. Dr. Hoffman not only helped get Caroline's second surgery scheduled in a timely fashion; he also "brought about the meeting of the minds that explained to us what rehab was all about and gave us some idea what lay ahead for Caroline."

Despite Dr. Hoffman's intercession, much darkness and confusion remained, including the huge unknown: where should Caroline go for rehab? The trauma team at Erlanger recommended Shepherd Center, but "what was Shepherd Center, where was Shepherd, and why Shepherd?"

"We found ourselves enrolled in a 24-hour, crash course in rehab hospitals," says Dick. "We tried to make a short list; maybe there was some place closer to home, like in D.C., or Baltimore." During the middle of this overwhelming process, Dick and Cheryl were visited by the Shepherd liaison covering Erlanger, who assured them that Caroline would be a "successful" patient at Shepherd—"whatever that meant," says Dick. But at that point it was time "to fish or cut bait," so Caroline would indeed go to Shepherd. "The decision had to be made—everything else had been put on hold, and we're a family of eight."

One other factor influenced the decision, says Cheryl. "I also went to Sewanee, and the father of one of my college friends, Dr. Edward Loughlin, was Dr. Apple's and Dr. Murray's former partner in orthopedics in Atlanta. My friend passed along her father's very strong recommendation that we come to Shepherd." In fact, Cheryl believes that Dr. Loughlin helped persuade Shepherd to find a place for Caroline. "He met us here. That was part of how we got here, and also how we were able to get in here so quickly—for which we are eternally grateful."

At Shepherd, the answers began to catch up with the questions. No one had more catching up to do than Caroline. Even her talk with the Shepherd admissions liaison at Erlanger had left her with many new questions. "She was saying, 'Shepherd Center would have great services to offer me. Most patients are at Shepherd for an average of six weeks; then they are prepared to go home. And I remember her talking about going on 'outings.' So 'I'm like, OK, mom, these are the clothes I need to pack for when I get back to school.' I mean, I had no idea what they meant by rehab."

Her first clue came shortly after admission: the American Spinal Injury Association (ASIA) sensation test. "They were doing all this sharp and dull pricking, muscle testing. I had no idea why." The next clue came the next morning, when Caroline's therapists already had her up and in her power chair, "going for a test drive." Inside the second-floor gym, "I see all these kids and other patients in wheelchairs; that's when it hit me, or began to. I think at that point I began realizing that there was something wrong with me other than a couple of broken bones."

Back in her room later that day, Caroline had her first visit from her rehab counselor, Cheryl Linden. "Cheryl came in with a model of the spine and starting telling me where my injury was and what the effects were. This was the first time I had heard I had a spinal cord injury, and all of a sudden we're having a huge talk about things that might never come back. I was in complete shock. I couldn't believe this was the first I was hearing about this."

If Caroline might have enjoyed a little time for recrimination and accusation at this point, she soon found that that's not what

Rehabilitation Counselor Cheryl Linden.

Shepherd is about. As Dick puts it, "When you get to Shepherd, time jumps to warp speed. We went from an environment of enforced immobility to the opposite extreme. We were dumbfounded." As Cheryl puts it, "It was total immersion."

In what seemed like no time at all, Caroline was into a regular therapy routine—"on a mat, stretching, assessing what I have and what I need to work on," as she puts it. "And eating," Dick reminds her. "That's right," continues Caroline. "Once they saw I had some wrist function, my occupational therapist, Cindy Hartley, immediately started me on a functional electrical stimulation program to get the wrist stronger. The next step was to feed myself instead of having my parents do it. It was kind of funny: If I could stab five pieces and get them to my mouth, that was a huge deal."

Caroline remained in the inpatient program for three months—longer than the average 45 days, but, in Caroline's case, that was a good thing. Her stay was extended because she kept improv-

Physical therapist Cathi Duggar.

ing. "I could feel myself getting stronger from day one," she says. She remembers the first time she could scratch her nose; she remembers when movement first began to return to her right arm. Then, in mid-November, after roughly two months in the program, a huge breakthrough: "I remember I was lying down on the mat, and they were stretching me, and I lifted my leg up and actually kicked the stool. Cathi Duggar, my physical therapist, said, 'Do that again.' I did it. I was actually starting to be able to raise and lower my leg on my own. That was a huge day in the gym. Then, when Dr. Murray saw me wiggle my toes, he wanted to extend my stay. I just kept on improving."

"Dr. Murray was incredible with Caroline," adds Cheryl. "He told Caroline that years ago he stopped telling patients what they could or couldn't do. He'd been proven wrong too many times."

With the return of movement in her legs, Caroline began training on the functional electrical stimulation (FES) bicycle and the Lokomat. "That was the best thing," she says of Lokomat training. "Feeling my legs moving and finally being vertical was really exciting, and Claire Hardigan, the physical therapist who ran my sessions, was so encouraging about my progress." The steady improvement continued to bring new goals within reach. Toward the end of her stay, says Caroline, "Cathi actually had me stand up in front of her," an accomplishment that meant concentrated work on "sit to stand" exercises, core strengthening, and—significantly— "standing transfers" in and out of her chair. "Transfers are such a big part of therapy," Cheryl observes, "such a big part of what you have to deal with every day. We bought a Hoyer lift to have available at home. But now it looks like we won't be needing it."

Home away from home for Dick and Cheryl was a rented apartment a mile from the hospital. Having their own lodging (rather than the apartments furnished by Shepherd) allowed visits from the rest of the family. Also, extended help came from Cheryl's sister, who drove up from Tampa right after Caroline's injury and who, says Cheryl, "did not leave my side for three months." When Caroline's inpatient program finally ended in December 2007, the family returned to Virginia for a very welcome Christmas holiday. Two weeks later, though, it was back to their second home in Atlanta, and Caroline enrolled in the Day Program.

"Three more months," says Caroline. "More physical therapy (PT) and occupational therapy (OT), more work on the Lokomat, and it was amazing how much stronger I got during the Day Program." The days were long—nine to four—but there was a difference now. At the end of the day, she got to go home to the apartment with Dick and Cheryl. "Sleeping in my own bed, eating the food Mom fixed—it was just like real life. And I loved it."

Caroline practices walking with her forearm crutches.

Candy Tefertiller, Clinical Program Manager, Beyond Therapy Program.

BEYOND THERAPY

"Actually," says Beyond Therapy clinical program manager Candy Tefertiller, "we have quite a few clients who have been in the program even longer than Caroline. For our purposes, as long as clients are making progress, remain motivated, and are following through with what we ask them to do, then we're happy to have them as long as they want to stay." She adds that once clients enter the program and see how much progress they're making, they do want to stay—"because they usually don't have another venue in which to do this type of neurological rehab."

Initiated in 2005, Beyond Therapy is yet another of Shepherd's boundary-pushing programs. According to Tammy King, Shepherd's director of outpatient services, "It really came from Montez Howard, our now-retired SCI program director. She said we needed another program out there because patients were coming back to her saying, 'Now what? What do we do beyond therapy?'" Its eagerness to answer this kind of question is exactly what defines Shepherd's mission—always seeking to better serve the needs of its patients, always seeking to extend the continuum of patient care. "Before this program existed," says Tefertiller, "it was really frustrating as a therapist because we had to send people home who had potential to go farther in their rehab. We just hadn't put together the best way to keep them going."

To say that the program is a success is an understatement. It continually operates at full capacity—between 30 and 35 clients, each of whom receives some 9 to 15 hours of therapy a week—and there's a perpetual waiting list 50 names long.

Beyond Therapy "keeps them going" by combining an expert staff (two full-time physical therapists and five full-time exercise physiologists), high-tech equipment, and the cutting-edge science of neuroplasticity. As Tefertiller explains it, "For years, we thought that after a spinal cord injury, the damaged nervous system had no ability to recover. So our job was to teach 'compensatory strategies'—how to compensate for not being able to use your legs, for example. Now, we're finding in a significant number of cases that providing the right sensory and motor training can help the body find new ways to activate muscle groups and facilitate recovery after an injury."

Of course, the potential of neuroplasticity depends on the severity of the injury, but, says Tefertiller, "as long as there is some movement below the level of injury, it's possible to help those muscles and that nervous system recover. However, full recovery may be limited by the amount of intact nerve tissue remaining after an injury. "

Tefertiller is quick to point out that the program also benefits clients whose spinal cord injury is "complete," whose nervous system no longer demonstrates voluntary motor activity below their level of injury. In these cases, the program's goal is to teach strategies for "lifelong wellness." Often, she explains, people with spinal cord injury have been sent home without a proper understanding of the importance of exercise, fitness, and how to maintain their health despite being in a chair. "So our job is to show them how to get back into a community fitness center, how to exercise, how to keep their body as healthy as possible in the hopes of minimizing any secondary complication that could lead to further disability."

To say that the program is a success is an understatement. It continually operates at full capacity—between 30 and 35 clients, each of whom receives some 9 to 15 hours of therapy a week—and there's a perpetual waiting list 50 names long. "We're unhappy that people have to wait to get in," says Tefertiller, "but at this point the program is still fairly new—the whole idea of this kind of program is still fairly new—and we're still trying to figure out how to best meet the patient demand for this type of nontraditional program."

Caroline is a great illustration of what Beyond Therapy can do. "When I first saw her, she was nearing the end of her Day Program stay," says Tefertiller. "I helped her primary therapist in Day Program use an ARJO walker, which supports the weight of her trunk and provides functional electrical stimulation on both legs to create a stepping pattern. She wasn't able to do any standing or stepping on her own, but she had a significant amount of spasticity—movement that's not voluntary but keeps the muscles very active and usually responds well to functional electrical stimulation. If she had had to just go home, without any such equipment and the knowledge to use it, it would have been very difficult for her to achieve functional improvement."

Tefertiller explains that Caroline and others like her are likely to start on the Lokomat, a robotic treadmill typically used for people who are not yet able to step independently. The robot helps move the legs in a normal walking pattern, with weight on the feet increasing as the client's ability and strength improve. Then, once clients develop the ability to help themselves walk, they move over to the manual treadmill system. Here, they will be supported in a harness system much like the Lokomat, but therapists on either side take the place of the robot, giving clients more freedom to do the work themselves.

At the same time, clients reap the benefits of electrical stimulation—whether on the functional electrical stimulation (FES) bikes or using the Bioness system to increase motor activity below the level of injury while walking and completing other functional activities. In the case of a patient like Caroline, whose legs tend to stiffen with spasticity, the Bioness device can produce a flexor response to initiate a stepping movement. The same company also makes an upper body device that helps open and close the hands. Beyond Therapy is extremely fortunate, says Tefertiller, to be able to offer the latest in rehabilitation technology. "Research is showing that both sensory and motor electrical stimulation may help the body recover. So we are improving strength and increasing motor activity, and at the same time creating a sensory awareness in the brain, saying, 'OK this muscle is active, so let's use it.'"

As for Caroline's progress, Tefertiller reports that in a recent therapy session "she walked about 50 feet without anybody holding on to her." It does help, says Tefertiller, that both Caroline and her mother, Cheryl, "are so motivated, so focused, and so positive about carrying through on everything we ask Caroline to do. They are truly an inspiration to the people here who get to work with them."

As the program continues to grow, Tefertiller and her staff are particularly excited about a big research trial on the immediate horizon. Thanks to a grant from the National Institute on Disability and Rehabilitation Research (NIDRR), the study will select 50 clients and follow each of them for six months. "It will stretch us," says Tefertiller, "but we're really looking forward to it. It will provide important feedback on what we're accomplishing here and should help with further funding and further expansion."

A problem loomed. As her three months of Day Program therapy approached their end, Caroline was still progressing, still improving, still getting stronger every day. She didn't want to stop; her parents didn't want her to stop. Actually, not a problem. Because it was precisely to address the situation of patients like Caroline—patients who continued to get better, to regain function, after the inpatient and outpatient programs—that Shepherd in 2005 had created Beyond Therapy.

Caroline's curiosity had been aroused when a fellow Day Program patient "who was making a lot of progress walking" told her that he planned to continue on into Beyond Therapy. Then, one day toward the end of Caroline's Day Program, Candy Tefertiller, Beyond Therapy's clinical program manager, made an appearance in the third-floor gym where Caroline and the other day patients were working out. "She hooked me up to this new e-stim equipment, Bioness, that we could use to create muscle contractions and break up the tone in my calf that made my legs so stiff. It was amazing equipment, and our idea was that I might be able to take a few steps with the walker. The next thing I knew I was walking all the way across the gym—with quite a bit of assistance, true, but I was getting my feet moving forward. It was really exciting."

Now Caroline had a "new goal to work on," and once her application to Beyond Therapy had been accepted, she had a new venue in which to pursue it. She reports to the therapy gym off the Livingston Gym, where she has a three-hour workout, four days a week. In addition to PT and OT, she works on strength-building with exercise specialists. "They work with whatever your abilities are," says Caroline. "Walking, squats, core work—anything you've got, they make stronger. And I keep on getting stronger."

After a year in the program, Caroline knows as well as anyone what the deal is: "to give you a chance to keep getting better and stronger." Her walking now is "amazing," she says. "I started off with that heavy-duty ARJO walker, then moved to a smaller version that still had a shelf on top to rest your arms, and then to a regular walker, and now I'm using crutches." Not to mention walking in the pool, which she believes is "helping tremendously." Caroline sums it up this way: "The whole program has changed my life."

"Everything just came together at the perfect moment," says Cheryl. "Candy is terrific, and Becky Washburn, the Beyond Therapy and ProMotion manager, has put together an amazing team. So now we have a whole other group of people we are just madly in love with. It just feels like a family down there."

When will it end? When will the Hazels return to Virginia for good? Dick and Cheryl don't know the answer to that question. As Dick puts it, "Caroline has gotten better every single day for a year and a half. Every week you can see it happening. It's hard to say, 'OK, that's enough.'"

"What we realize," Cheryl explains, "is that we've been able to experience something that not everybody does with a spinal cord injury. How fortunate that Dr. Loughlin sent us here, that we ended up here. We so feel like it's the best thing that could have happened. We have the option of going home, anytime, but we can't do it yet—not with all the progress Caroline continues to make. Even though it's very difficult on the family, for us not to be together. But we have this moment, and we have to get everything we can from it."

"I'm not ready to go home for good yet," says Caroline. "When you see this happening before your eyes, you want to keep going." She looks forward to the day when she can walk on crutches with just her mom spotting her, and when that day comes, maybe it will be time to go home. "Until then," she says, "we're living in the now, and I just roll with it."

Caroline with her aunt, Cathy Keating, (left) and her mother, Cheryl (right).

It helps that, for however long it takes, the Hazels have family at Shepherd. "It started from the day we walked in," says Cheryl, "and Alana Shepherd came up and introduced herself, within an hour of our arrival here. We cannot emphasize enough how much we love all these people, and it really is all about the people. There's Miss Barbara, the woman who took such wonderful care of Caroline's inpatient room—she prays for Caroline. All the nurses, the techs, Dr. Murray and Dr. John Lin, the therapists and exercise specialists—they have all contributed to Caroline's recovery. The ladies in the cafeteria, the security men, the people in the apothecary—we have friends wherever we go in this hospital, all of whom ask, 'How is your daughter?' That is the essence of Shepherd, all of these incredible people who have become a part of Caroline's journey. It's real, and it's been a huge part of her success, and of where we are today."

DOING WELL
DOING GOOD

S TAR
ATHLETE, STATE LEGIS-
LATOR, INFLUENTIAL LOBBYIST, SUCCESS-
FUL BUSINESSMAN—Rusty Kidd seemed always to be holding aces,
and, even with a half-century behind him, he was still at the top of his game.
Then the table—his world—fell out from under him.

After a weekend golf tournament for legislators and lobbyists in the
late summer of 1999, Rusty and several of his motorcycling pals headed up
into the mountains of North Carolina for a few days of scenic cycling. On
Tuesday, as he was cruising the Blue Ridge Parkway on his Harley, his front
tire slipped off the road. "Then," he admits, "I did everything wrong.
You're supposed to go ahead and get the other tire off the road and, if
necessary, head into the trees." Instead, Rusty tried to pull back onto
the road and went sprawling onto the pavement. "The first guy behind
me swerved and missed me. The next guy was afraid he was going to
hit me so he laid his bike down. Two things can happen. The bike can
skid smoothly along the ground, or its tires can grab, and it'll bounce
back up." The tires grabbed, the bike bounced up and landed
squarely on Rusty's back, breaking all his ribs, puncturing both lungs,
and crushing his vertebrae.

"From my own crash," says Rusty, "I got a scratch on the side of my
nose where my sunglasses broke. Had the guy behind me just rolled over
me, I would have had some broken ribs or a broken leg, something like that.
But he had to make a split-second decision, and I can't chastise him for that.
He broke his own shoulder in the fall."

One of Rusty's cycling companions was a doctor who grasped the critical severity of the injuries. "He got the emergency people to bring in a helicopter. He realized that if they had put me on an ambulance, I probably
would have died on the way to the
hospital."

At Twin Cities Hospital in Johnson City, Rusty almost died anyway. "My heart was going crazy. I was Code Blue three times. On one of them, my ex-wife and daughter had left the room to go get something to eat and heard on the intercom, 'Code Blue, Intensive Care.' They were thinking, 'Hope that's not Dad,' and the next thing they heard was, 'Will the Kidd family report to ICU?' I guess everybody figured it was over, but for some reason I refused to die."

Rusty stayed at Twin Cities for three weeks, until, as he says, "they were ready to get rid of me. Like most hospitals, it just wasn't equipped for spinal cord patients." Having served for many years as lobbyist for the Medical Association of Georgia, Rusty was well aware of Shepherd Center, and he also knew Dr. Apple—though, as he says, he didn't realize Dr. Apple was the "head honcho." He knew for certain that Shepherd was where he needed to be, so he had his family contact Dr. Apple to see if he could be admitted. "They let me in," says Rusty, "but they weren't happy that Twin Cities let me go so early. I wasn't stable enough to travel, but I made it."

Rusty spent three months as an inpatient at Shepherd, going through the tough adjustment—physical and psychological—to life in a wheelchair. He doesn't claim it was easy. "Initially my spirits were good," he says, "because, like most people, I didn't believe my injury would be forever. My first resolution, I remember, was that I wasn't going to shave until I could walk. Needless to say, I've shaved several times since then." Rusty remains thankful for the strong support he got during those hard days—not only from Shepherd's staff but from its incredible corps of volunteers. "They've always had former patients, peer supporters, ready to come in and talk to you," he says, "people of similar background or with the same interests or hobbies, to let you know that (a) there is life after injury, and (b) you can get to that life."

What Shepherd did then and what it does now, better than anybody else, is to get you prepared, after a serious injury, to go back home, to resume your place in the world. It's the premier place in the country to do that important job.

—Rusty Kidd

He also recalls with gratitude the support he got from friends and family—at Shepherd and at Twin Cities. "At Twin Cities I didn't even know they were there," he says of the friends and fellow lobbyists who sat for hours by his hospital bed. He found out later when they visited again, and again, during his stay at Shepherd. "Unless you've been in the hospital, you don't know how much that means."

As for family, Rusty's medical team at Shepherd liked to joke that his ex-wife was at his side more than most patients' wives, and he credits his injury with repairing the relationship between him and his daughter, Katherine, from whom he had been estranged since his divorce in 1996. In fact, Katherine spent so much time at her father's side during his rehabilitation that she returned to school and got a degree in recreational therapy from Georgia State. "Graduated magna cum laude," says Rusty. "A direct result of her time spent at Shepherd, and she even came back to Shepherd to work for a while, at Shepherd Pathways, the hospital's transitional living facility for acquired brain injury patients."

After his 90-day tenure as an inpatient, Rusty continued his rehab for another month as an outpatient. "I went down to what I call the halfway house, where you get an apartment and live with

Rusty with his daughter, Katherine, and his three dogs.

somebody while you figure out how to do for yourself outside of the hospital." Then it was time to go back to work at his lobbying firm, Kidd and Associates. He missed the first week of the 2000 legislative session—"mostly just pro forma anyway"—but was there for the second week. He had been injured in September and was back at the capitol in mid-January.

And that, says Rusty, is what Shepherd is all about. "What Shepherd did then and what it does now, better than anybody else, is to get you prepared, after a serious injury, to go back home, to resume your place in the world. It's the premier place in the country to do that important job." Important, he says, because getting back to work is "the best thing you can do."

In Rusty's case, the work environment is different in all the obvious ways. He can't negotiate the Capitol steps and can't get into some of the smaller offices. The chambers inside the building feature old, heavy double-doors that are difficult to open sitting in a wheelchair. "I can do it by myself," says Rusty, "but if somebody's around, I don't mind the help." And Rusty doesn't mind pointing out that he would much rather not be in a wheelchair, or that there are a few things that, if he could change them, would make being in a wheelchair a lot more tolerable. But the work is essentially the same, and he goes about it in the same way he always has—that is, with considerable success. He didn't lose any clients because of the accident, he says, even though he cautioned them that if they had any important issues on their agenda to let him know right away. "I told them I might get one sympathy vote. I wouldn't get two."

Rusty also believes that Shepherd, today, "with all the best facilities and equipment," is well positioned to pursue the elusive cure to spinal cord injury—perhaps through advancing technologies in stem cell regeneration. He admits that, after his rehab at Shepherd ended ten years ago, he sought far and wide for such a cure. "For a while there," he says, "you grasp at every straw that's out there. You talk to doctors in Guatemala, in Ecuador. I even had one come by my office and give me an examination." He also asked his sister, who at that time was a U.S. congresswoman, to talk to the head of the National Institutes of Health (NIH), to ask him, if it were his son, what he would do. "What this guy said was, 'Go see John McDonald at Barnes Jewish Hospital in St. Louis.' Rusty made an appointment and went to St. Louis, where he found out that Dr. McDonald was Christopher Reeve's doctor—and on the cutting edge of stem cell research.

Rusty thinks that, eventually, stem cells might provide the key to recovery from spinal cord injury, but, assessing his situation with typical candor, he no longer sees himself as a likely candidate for the procedure—if and when it becomes available. "I'm older now," he says, "got a pacemaker now that I didn't have before, not in as good a shape as I was. So who are they going to offer the operation to?"

That realization hit him hard, Rusty says, but it didn't stop him. Based on all the available evidence, it didn't even slow him down. When the legislature is in session, he's in Atlanta for the full term, in a motel suite he rents for the duration. During the rest of the year, he might be in Atlanta two days a week, or "whatever's needed to take care of my clients' issues." Otherwise, he's at his office in Milledgeville by ten o'clock in the morning, working away at his other full-time job—overseeing Middle Georgia Management Services, a business he created by merging a loan company he inherited from his father with one he had started himself. "We now have 17 small loan companies throughout middle Georgia," says Rusty. "Business is pretty good."

Then there's Job No. 3—less profitable but no less important. Rusty spends an inordinate amount of time helping other people—in many cases, but not all, other people with spinal cord injury. One form this service takes is that of a Shepherd volunteer, just like the folks who meant so much to him during his rehab. Shepherd calls him whenever a newly admitted patient looks to be somebody he could relate to. "Recently there was a politician from Louisiana, or it might be a doctor because of my work for the Medical Association of Georgia, or just about anybody from down in my neck of the woods." Just like he did ten years ago, says Rusty, "they need to hear that they can return to a good quality of life. I do that any time I can."

Sometimes the help extends beyond counseling. Rusty tells the story of "a nice young man from Milledgeville," Tyree Adams, who was a patient at Shepherd after being hurt in a car accident. Rusty stayed in touch with him after he returned home, and he watched with a sympathetic eye as Adams lost first his wife and then his job. But the man wanted to work, as Rusty tells it; he didn't want to be a ward of the state, so he decided to learn how to cut hair. A local barber took him on as an apprentice, but since a barber needs to look down on his client's head, cutting hair from a wheelchair didn't work. "I happened to have a stand-up chair," says Rusty, "which I loaned to him. He's been using it for

Tyree Adams cutting Rusty's hair from his stand-up chair.

a couple of months, and now that he has demonstrated the need, rehab is going to get him his own chair. So Tyree has been able to make barbering his new profession."

Then there's Rusty's house on Lake Sinclair, which used to be his fulltime residence until he decided that, for the sake of his and his family's peace of mind, he needed to live closer to town. The house is fully wheelchair accessible, and Rusty also worked with a company in Arkansas to design a specially reinforced boat and a ramp to get in and out of it without the fiberglass cracking. "Now other people in wheelchairs can use the house and the boat—maybe for a week's vacation. Something they might not have a chance to do otherwise."

Inside Milledgeville proper, Rusty has recently donated a piece of property to the city and is helping raise the money to build a facility for battered women. "I guess that doesn't have much to do with being in a wheelchair," he says. "It's just a matter of serving my little community in whatever way I can."

Rusty also serves the wider community, as chairman of the Georgia Brain and Spine Injury Trust Fund Commission, an organization that collects 10 percent of monies from DUI fines statewide and allocates it to the needs of people with traumatic brain or spine injury. "We are a payer of last resort," says Rusty, "based strictly on need. When private insurance, Medicare, and Medicaid have been exhausted, we come in and try to do what needs to be done to get that life as near to normal as we can." Of course, there's never as much money in the fund as the commissioners would like, but Rusty says that they will petition the legislature in 2009 to add a 10 percent surcharge to fines for parking in handicapped parking spaces, for riding a motorcycle without a helmet, and for reckless driving. "If the legislature will pass that," he says, "we'll be able to help more people."

Not surprisingly, Shepherd was a passionate advocate on behalf of the legislation that created the Georgia Brain and Spine Injury Trust Fund, and the connection is not lost on Rusty. "The people at Shepherd take the patient to heart. They do everything they can to get that patient back home, back to work, back to school. If they hadn't done that for me, I don't know how long it would have taken me to get my life together again, or to get to where I am now."

Where he is now seems, in Ted Turner's immortal phrase, "not too shabby." He has a successful career, an ex-wife that's a close friend, two grown children whom he "couldn't be prouder of," and dogs that are happy to see him when he gets home at night. Most important, out of a catastrophic accident, he's built a life that means something to a lot of other people.

Not that you're likely to hear Rusty Kidd sugarcoat the hard fact of life in a wheelchair. He admits to having bad days—days when he's not sure he wants to get out of bed. But with his full agenda, with people to help, with contributions to make, Rusty has good days, too. "And some days," he says, "are really good."

Rusty on his dock at Lake Sinclair.

New Directions
Spinal Cord Injury Research

Before coming to Shepherd in 2008, Dr. Keith Tansey had a perfectly good job—as director of the Spinal Cord Injury Program at the University of Texas Southwestern in Dallas. It just wasn't quite the right job. "Frankly, I was doing more time teaching and doing clinical work and less time doing research than I wanted," says Dr. Tansey. "So when Shepherd Center came looking for a director of spinal cord injury research, it sounded like a perfect fit."

Working with "great collaborating partners" at Emory and Georgia Tech (including what he calls "card-carrying neuroscientists"), the Savannah native has discovered in Atlanta "a great mix of spinal cord physiology, patho-physiology, patients, and engineers," adding up to "a really wonderful opportunity." With assurances from Mike Jones, Ph.D., Shepherd's vice president for research and technology, that he would be able to continue to combine human research with animal-model work, Dr. Tansey saw Shepherd as a place to pursue his overriding goal: "to be the bridge from the lab to the clinic, to get new discoveries to patients."

In a nutshell, says Dr. Tansey, the focus of the research—whether animal or human—is neuroplasticity—"that is, the changes in the nervous system that are related to functional recovery." And he believes that more fully understanding those changes has become fundamental to spinal cord injury research: "How does the system function with the connections that remain; or what kind of new connections does it try to make, and how do those new connections work?"

The animal-model component of the research is important, says Dr. Tansey, because "none of my patients have ever volunteered to let me slice up their spinal cord and look at it under a microscope." The human component is necessary "because you can't give a rat instructions. They tend to ignore you." Shepherd offers "the human lab research capacity," while his appointment to Emory medical school's departments of neurology and physiology provides "the animal lab capacity."

Dr. Tansey's expertise in neuroplasticity helps expand a new frontier for Shepherd's research efforts. He points out that Shepherd has long been a leader in "care research" as well as a key participant in large clinical trials "whether for drugs or cellular transplants or new devices like the diaphragm stimulator." But he sees his own work as representing "a piece that's not previously been here—the pre-clinical piece, where human subjects in the lab are doing things in parallel to what the rats are doing in the animal lab." In other words, rather than collecting data during the delivery of care or enrolling patients in clinical trials, "what we want to do is bring patients into the lab and study them exhaustively."

Two sets of tools are available for that exhaustive study—two sets of tools to measure what patients' nervous systems are still doing after injury, what they are capable of doing, how much adaptability they have, and what the impact of any intervention on their systems might be: electro-physiology and robotics. "With electro-physiology," Dr. Tansey explains, "we can keep track of when muscles are firing and in coordination with which other muscles, to what extent, for how long." Moreover, there's some extent to which electro-physiology can measure the brain's ability to communicate with nerve circuits below the level of the spinal cord injury. "So we can begin to find out what the wiring's doing, what's connected, what's firing."

Dr. Keith Tansey, Director of Spinal Cord Injury Research.

And at the same time, the robotic devices "can measure things like movements, how fast, how strong, what angle, all that kind of thing. So we have functional consequences of the neural activity—as we marry those two things together." The robotic devices also invite experimentation, says Dr. Tansey. "How does the nervous system change its function if we assist the patient in the activity; how does it change if we resist the patient?" Using such devices, patients benefit both from learning a task and from strengthening their ability to do that task—meaning that, beyond lab results, the robots "offer a therapeutic benefit in and of themselves."

Dr. Tansey says he's looking for an answer to "the question that bothers me: Why is it that some of the patients we work with get no benefit, some get a little, and some get a lot?" Answering that question means understanding more fully how different nervous systems act, which is exactly what he hopes his laboratory work will reveal. "The problem with recovery from neuro-system injuries," he explains, "is that it's very hard to know how much behavior is left over; how much is learning a new way around the problem, or compensatory behavior; and how much is recovered behavior. So our goal is to use these electro-physiology tools to measure how the nervous system is doing what it does as the patient is working on the robotic therapy."

To help achieve that goal, Dr. Tansey has proposed the idea of a dedicated spinal cord injury laboratory (or "SCIL," which he calls "an appropriate moniker"). Such a lab would provide the ideal scenario: having both the robotic and electro-physical equipment in the same place, as well as a team working specifically on these research projects. In addition to himself and associate research director Debbie Backus, that team would include a dedicated research therapist, a physiologist in the lab, resources for student stipends, and post-doctoral fellowships, "so we can have a whole army of people banging away on the future."

While Dr. Tansey foresees "a dedicated group of patients doing training protocols" in the spinal cord injury lab, he certainly hopes the lab would be used to measure the recovery of patients in other programs, like Beyond Therapy or the NeuroRecovery Network. Then, too, there is the forthcoming Geron stem cell transplant study, in which Shepherd is very likely to be asked to participate. "Let's say 10 patients come through, having had these cell transplants. We could bring those patients into our lab and glean a much richer spectrum of information about what the effect of the transplant has been."

Regarding the promise of stem cell transplants more generally, Dr. Tansey doesn't see a miracle cure around the corner. He welcomes the trial—the first ever to have FDA approval—and he

Dr. Brock Bowman and DPS

Associate Medical Director Dr. Brock Bowman is leading Shepherd's advance into one of the most exciting new developments in spinal cord injury rehabilitation: the diaphragm pacing stimulation (DPS) system. By means of minimally invasive surgery, DPS uses electrical impulses to stimulate the diaphragm, allowing air to enter the lungs. For spinal cord injured patients dependent on a mechanical ventilator, the result is fuller, deeper, more natural breathing and, best of all, a happy farewell to the cumbersome machine.

Dr. Raymond Onders pioneered the procedure at the Cleveland Clinic, says Dr. Bowman, "and we sent a couple of our patients up there to participate in the original study." Soon enough it became evident that the expertise could be shared. "Dr. Onders realized that since we have the largest SCI population around, it made sense for him to come down here and demonstrate his technique to one of our local surgeons." At Shepherd the procedure is performed by consulting thoracic surgeon Dr. Ezequiel Cassinelli. Dr. Bowman's role, he says, is to lead the initiative—"screening patients and following their progress afterward."

Thanks to its productive relationship with Dr. Onders, Shepherd became the next center to perform the DPS implant, and in 2007 Adam Booker became the first patient to undergo the procedure at Shepherd. Today, says Dr. Bowman, "Shepherd is a 'center of excellence' for the DPS system, which means that patients are coming here specifically for the implant." With formal FDA approval for the procedure having been granted in the fall of 2008, adds Dr. Bowman, "We stand among the very leaders in this area."

According to SCI program director Sarah Morrison, eight Shepherd patients had received the DPS system as of early 2009, with outcomes rated as "outstanding." In addition to the immediate benefit of patients being weaned from the ventilator, explains Morrison, "rehospitalization rates go down and infection rates go down. It is truly an incredible program."

What's more, adds Morrison, as the benefits of the program become increasingly evident, the procedure itself is becoming more streamlined. "We've just learned at a recent SCI conference that in the near future this surgery won't require an operating room. Doctors will be able to do it at the patient's bedside—basically an outpatient procedure."

The opportunity to be involved in work like this—with its supreme value on improving patients' lives—is what drew Dr. Bowman all the way from California to Atlanta. "I went to medical school to try to help take care of people," he explains, "without getting too bogged down in who pays for what, who's got insurance, and who doesn't. Here at Shepherd, I get to choose what I think makes the most sense for that individual. If they are covered, fine, and if they aren't, we usually find something else—like the money from Shepherd's great donor community. For me, as a physician, the mission is to take care of people, regardless, and that's what Shepherd lets us do."

respects the scientists at Geron. "They're topflight," he says. "They're being careful in their optimism, and they won't over-interpret the results." He also concedes that in animal trials stem cell transplants have enabled the animals to walk better. "The problem is," he says, "we don't really know why." The theory is that the stem cells will produce myelin, the insulation that surrounds the nerve fibers, to improve conduction. But, says Dr. Tansey, both humans and animals have "lots of other cells that can re-myelinate those un-myelinated nerve fibers." There is also a pharmaceutical agent that can make nerve fibers act as though they have been myelinated. "Yet it doesn't help many spinal cord injured patients. So I think that re-myelination is going to be of value to only a very small subset of patients, at best."

Explaining further, Dr. Tansey notes that rats are able to walk quite well with just the circuitry in their spinal cord, but that humans cannot. "So we really need something that's going to repair and improve the connections from the brain to the spinal cord," he says, "and we don't know whether this clinical trial will have that kind of result." That's why he sees such value in comparing the animal to the human model. "If you put in a cell, or a drug, and it makes the rat walk better, you have to ask 'Is it because the spinal cord is functioning better, or did [the cell/drug] improve the brain's ability to talk to the spinal cord below the level of the injury. It's a crucial distinction.'"

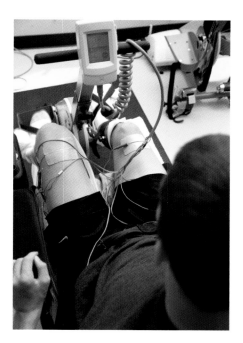

FES cycle that uses electrical stimulation.

That kind of question—left unanswered by stem cell therapy—will in the meantime be addressed by Dr. Tansey's research in neuroplasticity. "What we're doing will be applicable whether you're using physical therapy, or pharmaceutical therapy, or transplant therapy," he says. "Call it restorative neurology—focused more on using what remains than assuming that we will recapitulate what was lost." And even if we assume the possibility of repair, neuroplasticity will still be necessary "to retrain all those connections."

As an analogy, Dr. Tansey compares the lower neural circuits in the spinal cord that control the legs to buildings with parking lots. With spinal cord injury the parking lot empties out for the most part, but there are still a few cars here and there from local neurons and from sensory information. Those cars say, in effect, "Hey, the parking lot is empty, so I'm going to park in the spot closest to the door," so everything reorganizes below the level of the injury. Now, if you have some repair, if something is regrown out of the brain, it's got to try to find a parking spot—and it won't be the parking spot it had before. "It may even go to the wrong building," says Dr. Tansey, "so we're going to have to reshape and reorganize and guide those new connections."

In other words, neuroplasticity will continue to play a critical role in recovery—and in understanding recovery. To use another analogy, Dr. Tansey offers, "It's like learning a new language. You've got to make some new connections, store new information. A lot of recovery of motor function is relearning motor tasks, whether you are doing it with what remains or what you can regrow." In the last analysis, says Dr. Tansey. "Neural repair will not replace neuroplasticity. If one day we have repair, we'll have both—which will be great."

UPBEAT
DOWN EAST

❧

*I*F SHE WASN'T DOING
HER HOMEWORK, YOU'D BE MOST LIKELY
TO FIND CLARA BROWN IN THE GYM devotedly pursuing her passion—gymnastics. If not there, you'd likely find Clara engaged in one of her favorite activities—like track, or running with her mom, or skiing, or swimming. Of course, in Falmouth, Maine, the weather is not always ideal for outdoor pursuits, so on this day in the early spring of 2008, it was gymnastics, the indoor favorite.

Not that the homework had been shoved aside. The usual routine was to get to gymnastics practice early—go straight to the gym from school rather than going home first—then sit in the locker room and get her homework done before practice began. On this day, though, Clara had no homework.

"So I went on into the gym," as she tells the story, "and my coach and I started messing around. I was doing a handstand on his shoulders, and as he was walking around he tripped on something, and I fell on my head." Clara adds, typically, "He felt terrible about it."

Clara doesn't believe she completely lost consciousness but was "sort of in shock" for a moment. Then she realized she couldn't feel anything. "It was like I couldn't even tell that I was on the ground, so I sort of freaked out." A friend's mother was in the spectator room, says Clara, "and saw the whole thing. She called 911, and then the ambulance showed up."

Debbie Brown, Clara's mother, was at her law office in downtown Portland, 20 minutes away. "I was on the phone with a client, and my cell phone rang. I didn't recognize the number, so I didn't pick up. It rang again, same number, and I was still talking to my client so I didn't pick up again." Once she said goodbye to the client, the call came through on her office phone.

"It was Clara's coach. He said,

'I'm calling about Clara; she landed
on her head.

Clara with her friends at school.

She can't feel anything; we've called 911.' My heart stopped."

Debbie raced straight to Maine Medical Center, where her fear and frustration mounted. "When I got to the ER, they told me Clara hadn't arrived yet, so I went back out to the entrance where the ambulances come in and just stood there, waiting and waiting." When she finally called the coach to ask what was going on, he told her the ambulance had left the gym long before. "I went back into the ER," says Debbie, "and then they told me she had already been there. I was really upset."

What did Clara say when Debbie finally reached her side? "Mom, don't worry. I'm okay."

The mother still marvels at the daughter's fortitude and resilience. "She was trying to comfort me," says Debbie, "which is how she has been throughout this whole thing."

But in the meantime, communication difficulties continued. Clara's father, Greg, a pilot for UPS, was in a hotel room in Texas. "The good thing," says Debbie, "was that he was in the United States. Usually he flies in Asia. Still, he flies at night and sleeps during the day and doesn't always hear his phone ring. It took me an hour to reach him." At the same time Debbie, was awaiting the results of the Computerized Axial Tomography (CAT or CT) scan and trying to reach the family physician, also a close friend. He was out for the evening.

The CT scan revealed two compression fractures of the vertebrae—at C5 and C6—but no further information would be forthcoming until after an MRI. "We had to wait a couple of long hours for that," recalls Debbie. By the time that wait was over, the Browns' family physician had arrived, and he and Debbie sat down with the neurosurgeon. "A very difficult meeting," Debbie calls it. There was swelling in the spine; the central spinal cord had been injured, "and basically what he said was that there was really nothing to do right now." There was some good news: the neurosurgeon believed the fractures could be stabilized with a neck brace, and he reported that there were no pieces of bone fragment that would have required surgery to remove. "We were extraordinarily relieved that she didn't have to have surgery on her spine," says Debbie. "Still, his words to me were, 'All we can do now is pray.'"

Clara also remembers the uncertain diagnosis—and the uneasiness it inspired. "The injury was incomplete," she says, "but they were still worried. They hadn't seen a lot of injuries like mine and wanted to make sure I was prepared for the worst. For a while I couldn't really move anything, so I was afraid I might not be able to walk again." She spent three days in the ICU, then was moved to Barbara Bush Children's Hospital—a wing on the seventh floor of Maine Medical. During her ten days there, some movement began to return to her shoulders, "and I could wiggle my left leg a little bit—that was about it."

"Maine Medical is a highly respected hospital," declares Debbie; nevertheless, her daughter's hospitalization there was "without question the most difficult 12 days of my entire life." When it became clear that Clara had movement in her left leg, Debbie and Greg could not help but be hopeful. "If she had movement in one leg, we had to believe it would return to the other," she says, "but nobody would give us any kind of reassurance." She realized that the doctors were being professional and appropriately cautious, "but we were in agony the whole time we were there." The experience was overwhelming in every sense. Of course the parents wanted to be by Clara's side 24 hours a day, but at the same time they needed to become "instantly educated about spinal cord injury." A crucial element in that education was learning enough to pick the right place for Clara's rehabilitation.

The search began when the staff at Maine Medical directed the Browns to a couple of websites with information about spinal cord injury rehabilitation hospitals. "We quickly recognized that there didn't seem to be a lot of choices, especially for a child of 12 who didn't really fit into either a strictly pediatric program or an adult program," says Debbie. Shepherd Center was one of three or four hospitals under consideration, and Shepherd boosted its chances by sending a nurse liaison to meet personally with the Browns.

It was certainly the right gesture, says Debbie, "but that meeting, too, was very difficult." Shepherd's nurse, as Debbie explains it, came from an environment where many patients don't ever get out of their wheelchairs, so she conducted her interview with the Browns under the assumption that Clara, too, might be in a chair. "She wanted to make sure, for example, that our home was ready for a child in a wheelchair," says Debbie. "Which was understandable, of course, but we were adamant in our hearts and minds that Clara was going to be OK."

Finally, though, the meeting was about what Shepherd could do for Clara, and Shepherd's rep was able to reassure the Browns on several key points: Yes, Shepherd offered residential facilities so Clara's parents could be with her throughout her stay. Yes, there was a good possibility that Clara could have a private room. Yes, Clara's mom or dad could sleep in the room with her. Yes, Shepherd had a great adolescent program. "That was huge," says Debbie. "We thought if she were in an environment with her peers or even older teenagers, she would be pushed harder and motivated more than if she were with younger children."

A visit to Shepherd's website brought to light another critical factor: Shepherd's staff to patient ratio. "Greg and I, our family physician, the people at Maine Medical—we all agreed that that was extraordinary," says Debbie. "And when you add in the variety of rehab equipment and programs, well, it all indicated an intense dedication to the patient." Last but not least, says Debbie, Greg flew down to Atlanta two days early to tour the facility and came away sufficiently impressed to confirm their decision.

Having spent two weeks at Maine Medical, Clara found Shepherd "different." In the first place, at Shepherd she was surrounded by other people with similar injuries, from which she took new comfort. Also, after being almost entirely confined to bed, she mightily enjoyed the return to mobility—even if it was in a wheelchair. And there was one more point of contrast: "It was tougher," says Clara. "At Shepherd, they were immediately getting you up, pushing you to the next goal, and trying to get you to do everything you can on your own."

That's Shepherd Center's philosophy, get 'em moving, get 'em doing everything as soon as they possibly can. It was great for Clara. Every single day we were there, we saw some kind of improvement.

—Debbie Brown

The proactive approach gave the parents immediate reassurance that they had come to the right place. Debbie remembers that Clara was out of bed and in her own power chair on Day One, and how "ecstatic" she was to be able to propel herself around. "That's Shepherd Center's philosophy," she says, "get 'em moving, get 'em doing everything as soon as they possibly can. It was great for Clara. Every single day we were there, we saw some kind of improvement."

After a little more than a week at Shepherd, Clara had begun to put weight on her feet, though her right leg still needed bracing. "I got stronger fast," she says, and she gives a lot of credit to Shepherd's high-tech "locomotor" training—or weight-assisted treadmill therapy. "I really liked it. It was wonderful to be able to move without putting all my weight on my legs." In fact, during Clara's month of outpatient therapy, she took part in Shepherd's NeuroRecovery Network project, a partnership between Shepherd and the Christopher Reeves Foundation to study comprehensively the effects of locomotor training.

Debbie calls it an "unbelievably fantastic program"—through which, from watching her daughter participate, she came to understand the philosophy of recovery. "The fundamental idea

Clara with her parents, Debbie and Greg, her brother Spencer, and her sister Rachel.

is that if you can get those limbs moving again, if you can get those signals going back to the spinal cord and up to the brain, then your chances of recovery are vastly improved." She and Greg "definitely noticed the effects," and she's sure that Clara's rapid recovery of her balance, stride and overall walking ability had everything to do with locomotor training. "And the folks in the program," Debbie adds, "were clearly the cream of the crop—knowledgeable, engaged, helpful—and just had a great manner about them. They were so motivating for Clara."

In retrospect, Debbie describes Shepherd as "an amazing place," and she gives the hospital huge credit for Clara's recovery. She recalls with appreciation the kindness of Dr. Herndon Murray—"who really seemed to have a soft spot in his heart for Clara," she says—as well as the expertise of the therapists and nurses so dedicated to Clara's rehab and care. "However," Debbie adds pointedly, "I give primary credit to Clara. She has the most amazingly positive attitude and was always asking if she could do one more thing. And of course, Shepherd's staff embraced that attitude."

Dr. Herndon Murray
and the Adolescent Team

Medical director of the spinal cord unit, Dr. Herndon Murray has been at Shepherd pretty much since the doors opened—close to 35 years now. With all that history to contemplate, you might assume he would have to stop and think if you asked him what aspect of the Shepherd experience has meant the most to him over the years. But the answer comes instantly: "The adolescent team."

The concept evolved naturally enough, Dr. Murray explains. In the first place, there has always been a high incidence of spinal cord injury among teenagers, and as Shepherd began to devise ways of breaking its patient population into teams, it was easy to see that the kids did well when they were with their peers. "It became apparent that when the teenagers were working with each other and sharing the same issues, they responded much better," says Dr. Murray. "For example, a 60-year-old stroke patient is probably not going to be interested in toilet-papering Alana Shepherd's office."

Increasingly, says Dr. Murray, the adolescent team staff is focusing on prevention. "We've come up with the YIPES program [Youth Injury Prevention Education at Shepherd], where we're really trying to reach out to these kids and look at the ways they get hurt. Of course, prevention's not easy, but if we can prevent one or two spinal cord injuries a year, if we can prevent one or two kids from being paralyzed for the rest of their lives, it would be a great thing."

The program (and its website) is trying to warn teens about some of the most common causes of spinal cord injury—like head-first dives into unknown depths,

It became apparent that when the teenagers were working with each other and sharing the same issues, they responded much better. For example, a 60-year-old stroke patient is probably not going to be interested in toilet-papering Alana Shepherd's office.

— Dr. Herndon Murray

like not wearing seatbelts and safety helmets, like racing around on their ATVs. "These things are not legal on the roads, so the kids are tearing through the woods on them," Dr. Murray laments. "And this past summer (2008) we had three skim-board accidents. We had never had one before, and suddenly had three. What happened? Well, it turns out the kids were no longer content to skim along parallel to the beach. They started skimming into the waves. Of course, when they hit a wave, they do a flip—in six inches of water. So now we're trying to convince these kids that it's not a good idea to do a flip when there's no water to land in."

As for the adolescent team itself, Dr. Murray gives credit to Cathi Duggar, the team's physical therapist, and to Cheryl Linden, the counselor, for helping create something very special at Shepherd. "I really think the adolescent team is one of the things that set Shepherd apart from other rehab programs," he says. "Seriously, think about a family trying to find the right program for their injured child. Everybody has a nice building now; everybody's got a big swimming pool, the Lokomats and all those things. But when they see four or five teenagers out there together, laughing and smiling, and then they go to the next place and see a teenager surrounded by older patients in a general rehab setting, they're going to choose Shepherd every time. This program really is one of the things that make Shepherd better," Dr. Murray concludes, "and that's why I single it out as one of the best things I've been a part of."

Dr. Herndon Murray with his "team." Front, left to right: Ben Goss, Josh Fannon, Cody Holder, Dr. Herndon Murray, Rob Nelson, Jarred Cappola. Back, left to right: Sam Dowlen and Tyler Childs.

At the end of outpatient therapy, Clara was walking unassisted, even starting to run, and definitely ready to go home. She had missed a couple of months of the spring semester of her seventh-grade year and was excited about getting back to her friends and her school-work—not to mention being home for her older brother's high school graduation. She had a little math to catch up on during the summer but was ready to enter eighth grade with her class when fall rolled around.

First, though, Clara returned to Shepherd during the summer, for another month in the NeuroRecovery Network program. The therapy soon had her running two or three miles at a time, surely a joy for the young track and running enthusiast. But then came an odd and unexpected injury to her left hip, one that eventually necessitated surgery.

"Clara felt pain all the way from her hip to her knee," says Debbie, "and then her left leg began collapsing under her. The doctors at Shepherd thought it might be a combination of two or three pulled muscles, but rest didn't help, ice didn't help." It turned out to be a rare injury called avascular necrosis of the femoral head. Essentially, the blood supply had been cut off to the affected area. Clara needed surgery to have her hip "revascularized" by transplanting a portion of her fibula, along with the blood supply, up to the head of her femur—a procedure pioneered by a surgeon at Duke University Medical Center, which is where Clara went in December.

So Clara, after all, entered eighth grade in a wheelchair, which she admits was a "tough setback," and she's had to adjust her athletic plans. "I probably won't ever be able to run much, so I'm going to try to do low-impact things next year, like cross-country skiing." Characteristically, she's focused on the bright side: "It's great fun, and I really love it anyway."

Looking further ahead—post injury, post high school, post college—the plans of this remarkable 13-year-old are not definite, but the goal is clear: "I'm not sure how," says Clara, "but I know I want to help people."

NeuroRecovery Network

Shepherd Center's preeminence among rehabilitation hospitals was recognized in 2006 with its selection by the Christopher and Dana Reeve Foundation to participate in the nationwide NeuroRecovery Network (NRN). Partnering with the Centers for Disease Control and Prevention, the foundation chose only seven hospitals for the program, the purpose of which is to learn more about the potential of locomotor training for helping people with paralyzing injuries retrain their legs to walk again.

Selection in the program means a three-year, $450,000 grant for Shepherd, money that can add staff, upgrade existing equipment and facilities, and add an additional locomotor training unit. More important, it is yet another innovative program that helps Shepherd's patients get better—patients like Clara Brown and some 70 others like her. According to Sarah Morrison, physical therapist and spinal cord injury program director, "We've seen very positive results with nearly every person we've worked with. NRN participants are progressing more quickly in their recoveries, and more of them are relearning to walk on their own or with fewer assistive devices."

Josh Clift, from Australia, uses the Lokomat, a robotic-assisted treadmill with exercise specialist Mark Bowen.

What is locomotor training? This specialized therapy involves repetitive stepping exercises with body-weight support on a manual-assisted moving treadmill. Patients in the NRN program undergo an average of 40 of these locomotor therapy sessions; then the results are added to the database being compiled by the NRN project. The program benefits patients while adding substantially to scientific knowledge in the field of "intensive activity-based rehabilitation" of spinal cord injury.

Sarah Morrison's enthusiasm for the program is supported by the numbers. In the three years the program has been up and running (through 2008):

· The program has enrolled a total of 68 patients.
· At the time of their enrollment, 74 percent were dependent on a wheelchair.
· At discharge, 97 percent were capable of some level of community walking.
· 63 percent no longer relied on a wheelchair at all.

Sarah Morrison, Director of Spinal Cord Injury Services.

- 34 percent were community walkers, but relied to some extent on a wheelchair.
- And 3 percent used a wheelchair primarily but were able to walk minimally.

Given that the original grant from the Reeve Foundation was for three years, and that the three years are now up, will Shepherd be forced to withdraw from participation in this eminently successful program?

No, or at least not yet. As Morrison explains, "The foundation originally wanted to have each facility participate for three years and then switch out so as to reach as many lives as possible. The more facilities you have using this standardized protocol, the better, in terms of the research database being compiled." What the program's coordinators discovered was that the first year was lost to start-up procedures—acquiring the equipment, therapist and technician training, and putting the systems in place. Only in year 2 did the program's application really commence, with a consistent schedule of full clinic days. "As a result," says Morrison, "and because it's still a relatively new program, I think they weren't yet ready to lose the senior centers, like Shepherd, and they have just sent us a contract to extend the grant for another year."

And beyond that? "Well, we really don't know," says Morrison. "But Shepherd's volume of patients would be hard to replace. We see more patients per day than any other participant—an average of seven, versus four or five at most others. The inclusion criteria are very restrictive, so it helps that we see a great many patients to contribute to their database."

Still, according to the program's design, Shepherd will eventually be asked to retire. "And the world will not end," says Morrison. "We will continue to have a world-class locomotor program."

THE ACQUIRED BRAIN INJURY PROGRAM

Given the fact that roughly half of spinal cord injury patients also have brain injury, Dr. Donald Leslie (original medical director of the ABI program and now medical director of Shepherd Center) had long been advocating for a brain injury program. Newly hired CEO Gary Ulicny, arriving with his Ph.D. in clinical psychology, got behind the idea and the ABI program became a reality in 1994. Meanwhile, Susan Johnson had already developed a Day Program for brain injury at Shepherd in addition to an inpatient brain injury program at Scottish Rite Children's Hospital. So, in 1997, when Shepherd was looking for a program director for the brain injury unit, Ulicny and Dr. Leslie called on Johnson.

"The field is fascinating because no two brain injuries are alike," says Johnson. Certain guidelines and measurement tools—like the Rancho Las Amigos scale or CAT scans, for example—can help establish the severity of injury and chart the progression of recovery. But, as Johnson puts it, "the brain is mysterious."

The ABI program admits approximately 200 inpatients a year and treats another 300 to 400 outpatients. They've been in car accidents, or fallen from ladders or deer stands; they've been hurt on playing fields or been victims of violent crime; they've been electrocuted or suffered a stroke. And these days, they might have been blasted by an improvised explosive device (IED) in Iraq or Afghanistan.

"Because these folks are so different," says Johnson, "we've created very separate programs for the categories of injury: a coma program; a stroke program; an adolescent program; and what we call a care program, for people who have never gotten any rehab, and there are plenty of those, who need a tune-up or evaluation to assess what their needs are, to see if there is any possibility of any further recovery." Within the separate programs, patients are further classified into one of three "care paths," a designation that determines their length of stay: those with "mild" injury

Xavier Jordan, of Thomasville, Georgia, rides a trike in his physical therapy session under the watchful eyes of his therapy aid, Serena Yarbor (left) and his physical therapist Jennifer Smith (right).

Dr. Donald Leslie, Medical Director, Shepherd Center.

stay ten days or two weeks; "moderate" requires three to four weeks; and "severe" injuries might receive five to six weeks of therapy. Exceptions are made for coma patients, who might be in the hospital as long as three months.

Rehabilitation work is focused, intense, and often exhausting. "The work is highly structured," explains Johnson, "because so many cognitive issues are involved in completing tasks, in remembering, in focusing the attention." The structure is also important because the patients tire so quickly. "As these patients emerge and get better," she says, "it's like their brains are going a million miles an hour; they are concentrating so hard on the task at hand. Take tying a shoe, for example—they have to sequence it, organize it, and manipulate their hands. It takes every ounce of energy they've got. The axons aren't firing the way they used to, so these people have to think hard about every little thing they do."

The therapists on Susan's staff have the traditional designations—PT, OT, speech—but they're trained in behavioral and cognitive issues. "They have to know what kind of strategy will work with which patient," says Susan, "and it's very complicated. That's why we call it the silent epidemic. It's not a thing you can really explain. For example, the ABI patient might be up walk-

Georgia Dias, of Canton, GA, in recreational therapy with her furry friend, Kit.

ing around and you see him and say, 'OK, why can't you work?' Well, he can't work because he can't attend, he can't remember, he's disinhibited, he tells his boss he's a jerk."

Establishing strategies to work through these cognitive issues is the focus of the inpatient rehab program. Equally important is keeping those strategies in place in a real-life environment once the patient has left the hospital. This is where Shepherd's Day Program kicks in—and where Shepherd's dedication to "the continuum of care" sets it apart from other hospitals.

Once their inpatient program is over, most ABI patients still suffer some confusion and disorientation. To address these needs, to provide ongoing therapy, and, ultimately, to prepare these patients to reenter the world, Shepherd Center established Shepherd Pathways, which today is a 17,000-square-foot facility housed in adjacent two-story buildings on Clairmont Road in Decatur. In its Day Program, from 9:00 A.M. to 3:00 P.M., Pathways offers a full range of services and activities to foster the transition back to the real world—life skills training, vocational training, neuropsychology, and counseling. Therapists are there to work with patients one-on-one where necessary, but group work is emphasized so patients can learn from each other while readjusting to real-life human interaction. Recreational therapy is a huge part of the program,

Susan Johnson, Director of Brain Injury Services.

says Susan, "because we want them to get back to doing what they used to enjoy."

The Day Program has been a tremendous success, treating some 60 to 70 patients at any given time, but, typically, the ABI program was soon asking what more could be done. How about the patients who, after leaving the hospital, still needed 24-7 care but didn't have the family support? How about patients who couldn't get to and from the Day Program? The answer was to add a 12-bed residential component to Pathways, where patients without the support network can simply live, with the necessary supervision, while they continue to get better. The story of this addition exemplifies the serendipity that seems always to smile upon Shepherd Center.

The ABI unit originally established a Day Program at the hospital, but the need for an off-campus facility was quickly apparent. In 1997, Shepherd purchased a care facility called Meadowbrook on Clairmont Road and transformed it into the new home of the ABI unit's outpatient program. A few years later, says Johnson, when the idea of adding a residential component began to blossom, "Our CEO, Gary Ulicny, walked up to the house next door and asked the owner if he was willing to sell. Well, he was not only willing to sell. It turned out that his mother, who had just passed away, had received wonderful care next door, and the man honored that memory by giving us an incredible deal on the property."

Pathways has become an integral part of the ABI program's transitional effort, but the continuum continues to arc outward. Patients who have completed Pathways but still need structure in their day, still need cognitive improvement before they reintegrate into the community, have two further options. The first is Side by Side Clubhouse, a meeting place in Decatur where brain injured patients can get together and continue to work on their social and occupational skills. The

Gary Ulicny, Ph.D., CEO of Shepherd Center.

other option, for patients who have no family support, is Spring Creek House, a six-bedroom sup-
ported-living residence also in Decatur. Johnson describes it as a place where a person with brain
injury "who can't live totally independently, who just needs some help, can live indefinitely," and
where the round-the-clock staff can help patients work on reintegration skills like money management, continuing education, and transportation. The purchase of the house was made possible
through the generosity of Shepherd's donors, for which Johnson is particularly grateful. "It's really

Dr. Darryl Kaelin, Medical Director, Acquired Brain Injury Program.

quite amazing," she says, "that our donor support is such that we can see things like this happen."

A unique continuum of care, excellent and innovative programs, and remarkable donor support—if it weren't for hallmarks like these, Dr. Darryl Kaelin would probably still be in Indianapolis today. "I have to say, honestly," Dr. Kaelin declares, "that anybody who looks at Shepherd realizes not only that it is special but that it really has its priorities right. As I like to say, it practices medicine the way it's supposed to be practiced. If somebody needs something here and can't afford it, they get it anyway. That's really the wonderful thing about this place."

When the hospital turned 30 in 2005, Dr. David Apple retired as medical director, and Dr. Leslie, who had served as medical director of the brain injury unit since its inception, took over for Dr. Apple. In the national search that ensued, Dr. Kaelin emerged as the top choice to succeed Dr. Leslie as medical director of the brain injury unit, but it wasn't easy to lure him to Atlanta. Originally from Louisville, he had been medical director of Hook Rehabilitation Center in Indianapolis for ten years, from 1995 to 2005, and he was enjoying the challenge of building the first rehab hospital in Indiana.

When he began getting calls from Dr. Leslie and Ron Seel, director of ABI research, inviting him to come to Shepherd to interview, he says, "At first it was completely 'Thanks, but no thanks.' We were just about to build on a lake, I was really happy in my job, and there was just no reason to move." But the calls kept coming, and the discussions around the Kaelin dinner table began to lengthen. "We started to think, maybe this is the right time. The children were not yet in high school, and, being Southerners, we figured we would want to head back South at some point. So . . . ."

So . . . the Kaelins came down to take that look—with, from Shepherd's point of view, the hoped-for result. "I feel very blessed and fortunate to be the one who got the job," he says, "and it's been a great ride since I arrived in 2005." In less than five years, the number of beds in the brain injury program has grown from 18 to 30, not counting 6 additional beds in "the neuro-specialty unit" which, says Dr. Kaelin, are typically taken by brain injury patients. "So we're running at between 30 and 36 beds for our patients on a regular basis, which means that we've almost doubled our size—also doubled our staff in just those few years."

Shepherd Pathways is also growing, says Dr. Kaelin "to the point that we are looking for ways to expand our space" at the Clairmont Road facility. Then there is the most recent addition to outpatient services, the SHARE Initiative [see story, p. 82], dedicated to providing rehabilitation to the military service men and women returning from the wars in Iraq and Afghanistan. "The brain injury part of SHARE serves about 12 people at any given time," explains Dr. Kaelin, who directs that program also, "and as of early 2009 we've seen approximately 70 of these service people. So in terms of private facilities that are providing this kind of care, our program is certainly one of the largest in the country—after just over a year of being involved."

Dr. Kaelin also has a special interest in the research now going on at Shepherd to investigate the role of medication to help improve outcomes and speed up recoveries after brain injury. He is particularly enthusiastic about an ongoing study called ARMed to Succeed—so named because it is an acute rehabilitation medicine (or ARM) trial and also because it is a three-armed study, comparing two drugs to each other and also to a placebo. "So when you come into the study," he explains, "you have a one-third chance of getting a placebo, a one-third chance of getting Ritalin, and a one-third chance of getting Bromocriptine."

The rationale for the study is that both of those medicines have been shown to be effective for patients with brain injury, "but we don't know exactly to what degree." The three-year study will be by far the largest of its kind to date, looking at the effects of these drugs on some 100 to 110 patients who have recently been brain injured and are still in the hospital. "It should produce incredibly valuable data," says Dr. Kaelin, "on which of these drugs works better, on whom, and when. We're very excited about it."

Interestingly, Dr. Kaelin explains that both Ritalin and Bromocriptine increase the amount of dopamine in our brains, and that dopamine is "a common neurotransmitter" that gets depleted after brain injury, with a subsequent loss of focus and energy. "So the idea is that by replacing this chemical in [patients'] brains, we help [them] recover faster." The difference between the two drugs is that Ritalin is FDA-approved for attention deficit disorder, while Bromocriptine (trade-named Parlodel), has FDA approval for treating Parkinson's Disease.

Dr. Kaelin notes that pharmacology represents a promising frontier in the treatment of brain injury. "We've been dabbling in the area for many years," he says, "but most of the evidence we had was anecdotal, based on case studies of no more than a handful of patients." Thus the importance he attaches to ARMed to Succeed: "This will be the first big study to confirm that using

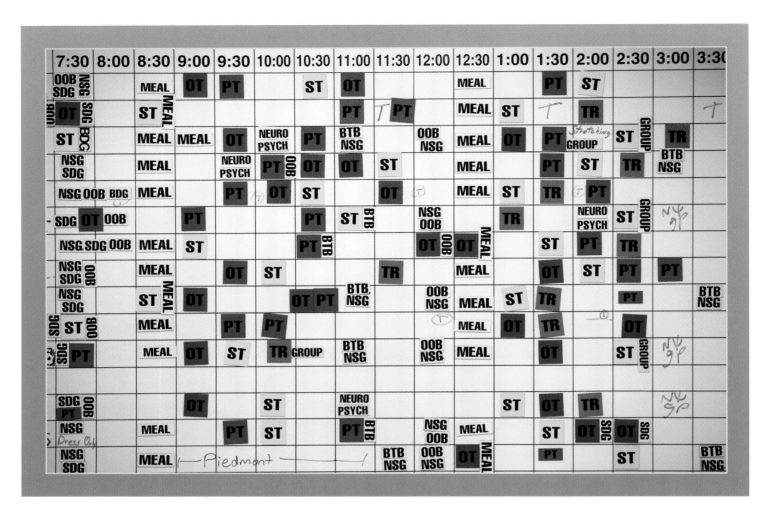

The busy activity schedule for the Acquired Brain Injury patients.

meds works better than not using meds—and that certain meds might work better than others. We've needed this badly."

Meanwhile, thanks to the efforts of Ron Seel, Ph.D., director of ABI research, numerous other studies are underway as well. One, says Johnson, currently ongoing at Pathways, is investigating "the bio-psycho-social issues of brain injury," closely comparing each patient's experience to that of his peers. "What are the differences? Why is the fatigue holding on in this patient more than in that one? What is interfering with this patient's progress? Is it the cognitive issues? Is it the psychological issues?" Answering these questions, says Johnson, will help establish best practices in pursuit of optimal outcomes.

Another grant has Shepherd's ABI program participating with those of nine other hospitals in a comprehensive statistical study meticulously tracking the results of various treatment and therapy programs. "You've got PT, OT, and speech all recording exactly what they're doing and how often. What the docs are doing, and what medicines they're prescribing." Statistical analysis of the entire body of data should help define what works most effectively. Johnson adds that "The study is already telling us very interesting things about stroke rehabilitation."

Clair Derr, of Columbus, GA, happily paints aided by her recreational therapist Ashley Haynes.

Anticipating continued growth, everybody in the ABI unit is delighted about plans now afoot for a design overhaul inside the hospital. "As the spinal cord unit expands into the new space on the fifth floor of the Woodruff Pavilion," says Dr. Kaelin, "our big goal is to get all of our brain injury patients onto the same floor"—namely the second floor of both the Marcus Building and the original Shepherd Building. "It's a one-to-two-year game plan, and we're in the process of raising the money for the renovation involved in that move right now. To have that kind of seamless operation would be a huge benefit."

After five years of the Shepherd experience, Dr. Kaelin remains as enthusiastic as the day he arrived. "You've got people here who are at the top of their field—physicians, nurses, therapists—who are not only very good at what they do, but who really love what they do. And that, I think, drives everyone to perform at the highest level possible. In turn, that desire drives the quality of the programs here. We are never satisfied with where we are; we are always looking to improve."

Johnson shares the sentiment "I love to develop new programs," she says, "and Shepherd has just let me do that. Sometimes my staff says, 'Whoa, Susan, whoa!' But what we've been able to accomplish in a relatively short period of time is really incredible. I feel like a kid in a candy store."

AMERICAN DREAMER

"SAUL ALWAYS MADE SURE TO TEXT US AT THE END OF EVERY RACE," says Yvonne Raisin. "Always. It might just be the two letters, 'OK,' but it was enough to let us know that the race was over and that he was fine."

Saul interrupts the story: "I remember one race where I crashed and knocked out half my teeth, and the nurse was going to call my parents. I said, 'NO, NO! You can't call her. I have to call first. If she hears your voice first, she'll freak out.'"

This time, there was no text message. There was no call. There was just a cell phone that refused to ring. "I knew it had to be bad," says Yvonne. "Jim and I both knew."

It didn't help that Saul, their only child, was an ocean away, in Angers, France. Yvonne and Jim could only sit in their home in Dalton, Georgia, and wait, in terrible uncertainly, for the text message or the phone call that would probably bring news that would break their hearts.

"The phone rang seven hours later," says Yvonne. "It was his team's manager. That's like hearing from the President of the United States. So I knew then that it really had to be bad. And then he told me I couldn't talk to Saul. He said, 'He's okay. Don't worry. I'm watching him. He's been medicated. He's resting.' I insisted on talking to him. 'No, no. You can't. He's in intensive care.'"

It's a long way from Dalton, a little town in the hills of north Georgia, to Angers, France. Saul Raisin will tell you the journey started when he was two; that's when he started riding a bicycle—without training wheels. Cycling was always the favorite family pastime; but it became more than that when Jim took up mountain biking,

Saul and his father, Jim at their family bike shop in Dalton, GA.

began joining in local group rides, and one day invited Saul along. "All of a sudden I was hooked, and, before I knew it, I had started racing."

When Saul was 18, and still in high school, he was selected for Team USA for the Junior World Championships in Portugal—the first real benchmark of his career. Soon thereafter, he was named "Best Young Rider" in the Tour de Georgia, which remains a favorite milestone because it was a significant award in front of what was essentially a hometown crowd. "So, for example, my grandmother could say, 'See, Saul isn't just a playboy. He does something for a living.'" For a professional cyclist looking to launch a career, France seemed like the place to be, so that's where Saul moved—by himself, barely out of his teens. "That's how driven, how goal-oriented he was," says Jim. "He knew what he wanted and had no qualms about just picking up and going to live in France. At age 20—talk about chasing your dream."

Saul quickly earned a spot on the French pro team Crédit Agricole. He made a name for himself on the "minor league" roster with a second-place finish in the Ronde de L'Izard—"that's a big race," he says—and was promoted the following year, 2005, to the top-echelon pro team, the major leagues. "Actually," he says, "I wasn't just promoted; I became the youngest team leader in the sport of cycling at the time." He justified the honor with a steady stream of stellar results: ninth place in the Tour de Germany, a top-10 in the Tour de Austria, a top-20 in the Tour de Switzerland—followed by his selection to the U.S. Olympic team.

Early in 2006 Saul scored his first major win, at the Tour de Malaysia, and came out of that race "in the best shape of my life." After that, he says, "Things get a little foggy." There was a race in America, the Tour de California that has been pretty much erased from his memory; then came the Circuit de la Sarthe in northern France, April 4, 2006.

Saul still doesn't know exactly what happened. He does know that he was in the final stretch of the first stage, maybe a mile from the finish, racing all-out. "Understand," he says, "nobody is side by side. There are 200 racers, wheel-to-wheel, full sprint. You're looking at nothing but the guy's wheel right in front of you. Apparently, we hit a bad section of road that had loose gravel all over it, and I just went down."

Yvonne adds that a sportswriter for a top newspaper in France returned to the crash site after the race to put together the details. "Her story was that the road had just been paved and that the left-over gravel was piled up thick on the roadside. In her opinion Saul must have hit all this loose gravel. They were really going fast." Saul agrees: "That's the only thing that makes sense." Yvonne offers the telling statistic that seven riders went down that day, three of them seriously hurt. "That race is always plagued with accidents," says Saul.

Saul suffered a broken clavicle, two broken ribs, and a mangled right hand, along with severe abrasions from the head-first impact that knocked him unconscious. All Yvonne and Jim knew was the little that the team manager, Roger Legeay, had shared with them: Saul was in intensive care at the hospital in Angers. Legeay's follow-up call brought worse news: Saul's brain was swelling. He was about to undergo emergency surgery. Yvonne and Jim needed to hurry. When they arrived at the hospital the next day, the doctors held out little hope for Saul's survival.

One fortunate coincidence helped avert their grim prognosis. The hospital at Angers happens to be a world-class facility—"the neurological center of Europe," says Saul, "kind of like the Shepherd Center of Europe." Only at this one hospital, he says, would there have been a neurosurgeon standing by to do the surgery he needed—"Professor Philippe Mercier, considered one of the best in the world."

The operation to reduce the swelling was successful, but Saul nevertheless remained in a coma for a week. For Yvonne and Jim, the anxiety of the situation was exacerbated by the fact that they knew nothing about brain injury—what it was, what it did—and no one in the hospital in Angers spoke English well enough to explain the injury to them. "It was terrible," recalls Yvonne. "They tried their best, but we just had no idea what was happening."

Even after he began to emerge, Saul's condition remained critical. He was extremely fragile; he was on a ventilator. When Jim and Yvonne were told to prepare to stay three months, they realized they needed to start looking for an apartment to rent. Then, unexpectedly, in his fourth week, Saul turned the corner. "He came off the ventilator and was able to sit up in a chair, and they told us the danger of his dying had passed," says Yvonne. "The moment we heard that, we began planning to bring Saul home."

Saul was still far from clear about what had happened, where he was, or why. Fortunately, however, the cycling community worldwide was very well aware of what had befallen one of its bright young stars. The Tour de Georgia happened to take place right after Saul's accident, and when it came through Dalton, the racers honored Saul by tying green ribbons—his team's color—to all the bikes and dedicating a mountain bike park in his name. Local coverage of the event caught the attention of Dottie Boring, who happened to be not only a close friend of Saul's grandmother but also a longtime supporter of Shepherd Center.

Alerted by Ms. Boring to Saul's situation, Shepherd made arrangements to have Saul flown to Atlanta via air ambulance. For Yvonne, it was like the end of a long, dark night. "From the minute we hit the door at Shepherd, it was unbelievable. Always a smile on every face. Always 'How are you doing? How did you rest?' Before, we knew nothing. At Shepherd, they tell you every detail about what your loved one is going through and what they are doing about it. We felt so wanted there."

For Saul, the fog was still thick. He remembers a day, early in his rehab, sitting in his wheelchair and trying to put his socks and shoes on. "They were just slip-on Crocs, but I couldn't do it. I remember looking up and seeing my parents in tears, and I didn't know why." In fact, Saul only became fully aware of what had happened to him after several days at Shepherd. He got on the Internet to check his e-mail and found that he had more than a thousand messages from cyclists all over the world, including Lance Armstrong. "They were all saying, 'Saul, we just want you to know we're praying for you and we're here for you.'" Further Internet investigation turned up a CNN story with all the details. "I finally understood why I was in a wheelchair," he says. "I finally realized I had a brain injury."

No matter what time of day it was— noon, midnight, two in the morning—everybody always had a smile on their face. It was wonderful. We need more Shepherd Centers in the world.

—Saul Raisin

That was why he stayed so exhausted. That was why the intense effort it took to try to add "five plus two" made him want to go back to bed. And that was why his therapists constantly challenged him with a new goal. "It was probably the second day I was there, and they were already saying, 'Saul, we're going to make some goals.' I told them my first goal was to be able to lift my head off my pillow."

Actually, though, asking Saul Raisin to meet goals is like throwing Br'er Rabbit in the briar patch. His first huge goal was to walk to his mother on Mother's Day, May 15, less than a month and a half after his accident. He did it: four steps into Yvonne's arms. "After that," he says, "my goal was to ride my bike again. Other doctors might have discouraged me, but Dr. Bilsky told me to go for it."

That would be Dr. Gerald Bilsky, who was in charge of Saul's rehabilitation at Shepherd Center, and to whom Saul's family still expresses the deepest appreciation. "We maintain he was the reason Saul got well," says Yvonne. "He never told Saul he wouldn't be able to ride his bike, never put any limits on what might lie ahead." Dr. Bilsky's precise words, as Jim recalls them, were,

"Let's don't take it away from him. Let's just see what happens."

After four weeks of inpatient therapy, Saul continued his rehabilitation at Pathways, Shepherd's special outpatient facility where patients with brain injury can continue their return to independent living. Then it was time to get on with it. He calls graduating from Pathways a more memorable event than graduating from high school. He had new goals to set, new dreams to pursue, and over the past two years the list of his achievements is astounding.

Tops on that list is his Raisin Hope Foundation, whose Website, RaisinHope.org, is now up and running. The subhead under the title on the homepage, "A place for traumatic brain injury (TBI) information, support and hope," says it all. As Saul explains, "While I was still in the hospital, I told my friends and family that if I ever had a normal life again I want to give back and help people who've been through this kind of injury." In fact, Saul was still in rehab when he hatched the idea of a charity ride for brain injury. The response was overwhelming, and the first annual Raisin Hope Ride took place exactly one year after Saul's injury—with all proceeds going to brain injury treatment and research.

Now Saul spends part of every day on foundation work—reaching out to others with brain injury, expanding the network of links to brain injury information resources, and raising money for brain injury research. "At Raisin Hope," says Saul, "we don't have all the answers, but we can definitely be a shoulder to lean on, a support group; we can listen and say, OK, we've been there."

Then there's the book, *Tour de Life: From Coma to Competition*, coauthored with novelist and cycling expert Dave Shields, published in 2007. This inspiring narrative offers a remarkably vivid account of Saul's near-fatal crash, his against-all-odds recovery, and the superhuman effort he expended in pursuit of his ultimate dream: to rejoin his team and ride in the Tour de France. The same motive, says Saul, drove the writing of the book and the creation of the foundation: "to tell people my story, to let them know they can get through this kind of injury, to let them know they're not alone."

Since the book's publication, Saul's dream has taken a new shape. Though he did return to France and train with Crédit Agricole, team doctors ultimately refused to sanction his return to the dangerous world of professional racing. At first crushed by the news, Saul has come to see the wisdom of their decision: "They were right. I don't need to risk my life for cycling."

Instead, says Saul, beginning in 2009 he will be a professional triathlete/motivational speaker, with the immediate goal of competing in the Iron Man competition in Hawaii. Characteristically, his daily training regimen begins at 5:30 A.M. with a 2.5 mile swim. Then it's on to biking and running (the other two events that compose a triathlon). He trains six days a week, four to five hours a day. In November 2008, he put a wrinkle in the schedule. He flew to New York and ran the New York City Marathon—all 26.2 miles.

As for the other career, motivational speaking, the date book is filling up: In January, the Brain Injury Association of Tennessee and Safe Kids in Atlanta; in February, Lifetime Fitness in New York; in April, a U.S. Air Force leadership conference in Colorado Springs. He has already been to the brain injury ward at Walter Reed Hospital to talk to the soldiers there and sign copies of his book, and he's also looking forward to participating in the Wounded Warrior Project, a bike ride in Miami to raise money and awareness for brain injured veterans.

Sound like a full schedule? Saul is confident he can handle it, and he gives credit for that confidence to Shepherd and to Dr. Bilsky. "Shepherd is a symbol of hope," says Saul, "hope that you can still pursue your dreams. As Dr. Bilsky kept telling me, 'I wouldn't bet against it.'"

DR. GERALD BILSKY

"His mother was going to kill me, but Saul was determined," That's how Dr. Gerald Bilsky remembers the dynamic surrounding Saul's dream to return to competitive riding—and Dr. Bilsky's unwillingness to take that dream away from him.

On Shepherd's medical staff for a dozen years now, Dr. Bilsky likes a full plate. He not only sees patients in both the acquired brain injury unit and the spinal cord injury unit but also serves as medical director for outpatient services. "That is," he explains, "all the outpatient clinics here in the building—including MS, the pain clinic, urology, wound —pretty much everything we do. We see somewhere between 50 and 100 patients a day, between the various disciplines."

Dr. Bilsky describes his work at Shepherd as a "diverse occupation, with my hands in a lot of different things," and he'll tell you that on the typical day he's likely to be "the first one in the building on the medical side." But he's not complaining. "I like what I do and I like the people I work with," he says. And, emphatically, he likes Shepherd Center.

There is an upbeat, positive ambiance here that you don't see—even in other rehab places.

— DR. GERALD BILSKY

"In the first place," he explains, "it is a milieu unlike any other I've ever seen. There is an upbeat, positive ambiance here that you don't see—even in other rehab places. Given that we're a catastrophic care hospital, people often say, 'Wow, isn't it depressing to work there?' But you walk in the building, and you find something very different."

In the second place, there is the level of competence, of expertise, that prevails at Shepherd. As Dr. Bilsky puts it, "We help families. We know what we're doing and we're pretty good at it."

And finally, "what is really unique," says Dr. Bilsky, "is the Shepherd family. James is here, chairman of the board. Alana is here, founder of the hospital. And they often get to know more about various patients we have here than the people who are actually working with those patients. That's really amazing."

To families like Saul Raisin's, Dr. Bilsky offers one assurance: "I can't promise results," he says, "can't promise outcomes—but I can promise that the people here care. That's the most important thing: the people here do care." Saul, Yvonne, and Jim Raisin will happily bear witness.

It was Saul's first team manager in France who gave him the nickname "American dreamer." When he returned to France to train for his return to competition, his best friend on the team, Lionel Marie, urged him on with the words, "Keep dreaming."

Lionel doesn't need to worry. Nobody dreams bigger—or works harder to realize his dreams—than Saul Raisin.

THE MARCUS COMMUNITY
BRIDGE PROGRAM

Yes, the spinal cord unit has its Day Program and its Beyond Therapy. Yes, the acquired brain injury unit has its Pathways and its SHARE Initiative. Yes, Shepherd is Shepherd because of the range, the reach, and the excellence of its patient programs. But in 2000, the year of the center's 25th birthday, Shepherd's continuum of care was defined for the 21st century. In April of that year, the Marcus Foundation approved a $17.6 million grant—the largest single gift in the hospital's history—to establish the Marcus Community Bridge Program.

Unprecedented in scope, the program's intent is to provide up to 12 months of follow-up care to virtually every patient who comes though Shepherd's doors. More specifically, the program insures the best possible transition-to-home services for departing patients—including telemedicine technology, vocational services, self-care education, and therapeutic recreation in clients' own communities.

"It's the only one of its kind in the medical field," says Chief Nurse Executive Tammy King, who directs the Bridge Program. "I know because I did a literature search when I first started it. There are smaller programs around, targeted specifically to this or that, like cardiology or cancer, but in terms of the length of our follow-up, the degree of our support, how far out there we go, there's not another program like it in the entire nation."

Interestingly, that $17.6 million was meant to fund the program for eight years at 2.2 million a year—meaning that, today, the money should have been spent and the program shuttered. That hasn't happened, thanks to King and her staff. King realized that by husbanding those resources, the program could be lengthened and strengthened; there would be more community buy-in, and patients would ultimately reap richer benefits.

For example, says King, at first the program sent everybody home with expensive equipment—computers, video monitoring, etc. "But then it occurred to me: You know what? Not everybody needs this. What's more, if they do need something like a computer, I rely on community and regional resources first, then turn to Bridge money." Here's the incredible bottom line: For every dollar of Bridge money they spend, King and her staff find $6.50 in the community. "So," says King, "the program that was scheduled to run out of money in eight years still has half its funding left."

Such stewardship is good for the program and good for the patients, who are thereby discouraged from adopting "that entitlement mentality." "We stick to the mission," says King. "We help the family and do everything we can to get them what they need, but it doesn't work if they're not doing everything they can do also."

How does it all work? King has more good stories than time to tell them, but here's one good one. A physical therapist recently came to King with a problem: She had a patient who needed a special bed but didn't have the durable medical equipment insurance. Plus, he was headed up to Maine. What could she do? "Well," says King, "one of my girls has that region, so she calls a vendor up there and says, 'John, I need this bed. It costs $10,000. What can you do for us?' John says, 'What can you pay?' She pulled a figure from out of space somewhere: 'Three thousand dollars.' John says, 'Okay.'

Tammy King, Chief Nurse Executive and Director of the Marcus Community Bridge Program.

The Bridge Program might have covered the $3,000, but, again, says King, "We don't like doing the entitlement thing. We went back to the family and said, 'We can pay $1,500. Can you pay $1,500?' And they said, 'Yeah, but not all at once. Can we pay $100 a month?' So we got $100 a month from them for 15 months, and we paid the other $1,500, and this kid got his mattress."

As another illustration of the program's unpredictable magic, King tells the story of a patient in Florida "who needed to come here in the worst way." How could she and her team get him here? "We called a family whose own son is a quad and said, 'Remember that favor you said you would do for us?' They said, 'Of course.' We said, 'Well, here it is. If we pay for the gas, will you bring this person up here?' It was like 'Boom!' In a heartbeat! Because it's just a big extended family out there."

It's all about "pulling people in" and making connections. King mentions a patient who received $5,000 from the Brain Injury Trust Fund to remodel his house in Social Circle, Georgia, to make it wheelchair accessible. When his Bridge caseworker realized how woefully inadequate those funds would be, says King, she pulled several organizations together—Easter Seals, Housing and Urban Development, and Goodwill—and turned the remodeling into an $85,000 rebuilding project. "We were able to put the package together for them," says King.

These and dozens of other such stories explain why the Bridge Program, rather than going broke, continues to serve about 400 patients a year—and continues to make the lives of those patients, post-discharge, as productive and fulfilling as possible. Maybe one day the program will meet its unstated goal of convincing insurance providers that the services it provides should be reimbursable. Indeed, some progress in this direction has been made. King says she now has contracts with two insurance companies as well as workers' compensation customers. In the meantime, the Bridge Program's great work will continue, and its welcome reach will expand. To date, the Bridge has served patients across 19 states. Program satisfaction stands at 100 percent.

MUSIC TO HIS EARS

*P*ARKER
KING DOESN'T REMEMBER
THE ACCIDENT THAT ALMOST TOOK HIS
LIFE back in the summer of 2003, but he knows the story. A couple of weeks
before the beginning of his senior year at The Lovett School in Atlanta, he drove
over to Athens to visit his brother, a freshman at the University of Georgia. Parker
can tell you the accident took place at night, that he was a pedestrian; that he
must have slipped off the curb, tripped, and gone sprawling right in front of an
oncoming pickup truck. "But from that night and for the next two and a half
months," says Parker, "I really don't remember much at all."

Parker's mother, Betty, an accomplished artist, was painting in
Taos, New Mexico. His father, Rob, was traveling in Florida. By the time
Rob got hold of Betty, it was the middle of the night. "I was sound
asleep," says Betty. "It was the phone call every parent lives in dread of.
All Rob could tell me was, 'Parker's been in an accident. It's his head.
And we have to pray.'"

The trip from New Mexico to Atlanta to Athens was excruci-
ating, says Betty, because she knew so little about what had happened
and what, exactly, her son's condition was. What she discovered when
she got to Athens Regional Hospital did little to lift her spirits. "By the
time I got there, Parker had already had brain surgery. He had a de-
pressed skull fracture, so they had to go in and relieve pressure on his
brain." Parker also had a broken neck and severe internal injuries, including
a lacerated liver. "The doctors told us that either the brain injury or the liver
injury could take his life at any moment," recalls Betty. "So we kept praying."

Parker was in Athens Regional for two days and then spent a week at
Grady Hospital's Level One trauma unit. From there he was transported to
Emory's ICU, where surgeons repaired the fracture in
his neck. "It's called a hangman's
fracture,"

he says, "because it cuts your oxygen off unless somebody gets to you real quick." Five years later, Parker still has a small scar from the operation.

The King family had long been familiar with Shepherd Center. Betty was a high school classmate of James Shepherd's younger brother, Tommy, and she remembers well James's own accident and the hospital that grew out of it. Also, Betty's stepfather, Bill Hatcher, is a former Shepherd board member. What the Kings did not know was that Shepherd had an ABI program. "We called Shepherd immediately because of the broken neck," says Betty. "Luckily, it turned out that he didn't need Shepherd for that. But when we made that call, we learned that Shepherd also treated brain injury."

Parker was admitted to Shepherd three and a half weeks post injury—awake, but extremely confused. He remembers little from those days, but he does remember his music—probably because music had always been at the center of his life. "We knew how much his music meant to him," says Betty, "so early on at Shepherd we got him some earphones and some of his favorites— Grateful Dead, Moody Blues—nothing too loud or heavy but things he really liked. We could see him mouthing the words before he was really talking again." Betty also recalls with amusement that while Parker was still at Grady, a friend brought him a relaxation CD, "some kind of spa music." He was still just semiconscious, and when the music started playing, says Betty, "I could see this expression on his face, like he had just bitten into a lemon, or like he was in some horrible pain." Neither she nor the nurse could imagine what was the matter, until the nurse finally asked, "Is it the music?" and Parker nodded yes. "Honestly," says Betty, "Parker's loathing of that spa music was one of the first things he communicated to us."

More seriously, Parker believes that music—his music—did much to abet his recovery during those early days. "It was the only organized thing going on in my mind," he explains. "It was also familiar, when everything else was confused, scrambled, and chaotic. It helped me relax and calmed me down. That was a real key."

Parker has another early memory—of a sensation that he recalls as an image. "I felt like I was under water and everybody else was above, out of the water, on dry ground. I was trying to reach the surface, trying to swim up to where everybody else was but couldn't quite get there yet." Parker adds that the important thing was that the sensation did not make him feel frustrated or panicky. "Actually, I was aware that I was getting closer and closer. I was slowly getting there." Betty, who has become a mainstay as a volunteer in Shepherd's Family Support Services, says she uses this description frequently when talking to the families of brain-injured patients. "It gives them something to relate to, an image that they can comprehend in terms of what their loved one is going through."

Nor does Parker remember much about those first days in therapy, about having to search the schedule board posted on the wall in the ABI unit, looking for his own name and his rehab assignments for the day. "I only remember one," he says. "BTB. Back to bed. That was my favorite."

Watching the process day after day, Betty learned that teaching the brain to function again is an exhausting ordeal. Every morning would begin with Parker being asked to read a sign posted in his room telling him the day and the date. "Once he looked away, they would ask, 'Parker, what day is it?' And at the beginning, he wouldn't be able to answer, so they would start all over again."

"Yeah, I kind of remember that," says Parker. "Every morning when they woke you up, the first thing they asked you was, 'Where are you, what happened, what day is this?' Every morning."

To which Betty adds, "I remember when you left, you said, 'I'll never know what day it is the way I knew what day it was when I was at Shepherd.'"

Mostly what both Parker and Betty remember is Parker's steady progress, the gradual improvement day after day. While Parker recalls it generally—"I remember every day being better than the previous one"—Betty can tick off the milestones of Parker's recovery: taking his first step, writing his name, reading with some comprehension. A big one, she says, was when he began to have "new memories," as opposed to memories from before the accident, because that meant his brain was processing current information. "It sounds funny to say it, but it was so exciting, because every day there was something to celebrate."

To illustrate, Betty recounts the day Dr. Donald Leslie, who was in charge of Parker's rehab, was in the therapy gym with Parker and another patient Parker had gotten to be friends with. He gave them a

Betty King, Parker's mother.

word—some medical term, as Betty remembers it—and told them that whoever could remember the word the next day would get a dollar. He told them to really work on it, all day long and all night long. Well, Parker worked on it, and, the next day, when Dr. Leslie popped the question, "Parker blurted out that word in an instant."

Parker finishes the story: "Of course, it wasn't the dollar. I just wanted to remember. I wanted to get better. I was so determined to get better. I tried hard every single day." When the nurses or therapists told him to do this or that, Parker always had one reply: "'Whatever it takes.' That was my mantra."

The most obvious sign of Parker's progress was the look in his eyes. "At the beginning, he had no expression," says Betty. "By the end of the month he was Parker again. The twinkle was returning to his eyes, the sense of humor was coming back." Not that she would want Parker or anybody else to have to go through such an ordeal, but Betty took a profound joy from the experience of witnessing his recovery. "It's an incredible way to learn about life, to be reminded of what most of us take for granted every day. Really, for me it became a very spiritual journey."

Next on Parker's rehabilitation schedule was six weeks of outpatient therapy at Pathways. Rob dropped him off every morning, and Betty picked him up in the evening, "kind of like taking him to school," except that, at the beginning, Parker's therapists took him from one class to the next. By graduation, though, it had become very much like school, with Parker responsible for knowing his own schedule and for getting himself to the right class at the right time. "Getting him more independent was the whole point," says Betty, "and you could see a huge improvement."

With the turning of the new year of 2004, real school loomed. The spring semester of his senior year was beginning, and Parker was determined to graduate with his class. "I didn't think he was ready," says Betty.

"But I had to go," says Parker. The good news was that Parker had always been a good student, had taken summer school courses to get ahead, and needed few credits to graduate. The bad news was that the major obstacle was senior English, requiring the kind of comprehension that was most slow to return. "I mean, we were doing The Canterbury Tales in Old English—that kind of thing."

Betty would drop Parker off at school, then come home and study the English assignment to prepare for the evening's homework session. "As I remember that semester," says Parker, "it was mostly a matter of hard academic work, struggling to get through it, with my mom giving me a lot of help." One thing he remembers very well, though: "I walked across the stage with the rest of my class. It was a great moment."

Parker spent the next year outdoors, fully rehabilitating his body as his mind healed at its own pace. First came a Lovett alumni trip—three weeks in a cloud forest in Ecuador. Next came a more daunting outing: three months in the Himalayas, including two and a half weeks of camping at altitudes as high as 17,000 feet. Then, in the spring of 2005, the year after graduating, Parker was off once more, on a National Outdoor Leadership School trip to New Zealand. "It was another three months," he says, "and even more physically demanding,"—including a solid month of camping in New Zealand's Southern Alps, two weeks of sea kayaking, and three weeks of coastal sailing. "I loved it all," he says, and then pauses to reflect: "You never know what's coming. You might fall off the curb and get run over by a truck at any minute. So my mission is to get out there, see some things, and never waste an opportunity."

I say all the time, Shepherd gave Parker his life back. It's not just that the people are top notch, it's also the attitude. I can't stress how important that is...that positive energy all around you just feeds you and makes you want to do better.

—Betty King

After devoting the "gap year" to physical rehabilitation, it was time to return to the classroom. Parker spent two years at Fort Lewis, a small liberal arts college in Colorado (that happened to have a great outdoor program), and then, in the fall of 2007, transferred to the University of Georgia. After a year and a half in Athens, Parker came to the conclusion that the university was throwing up too many obstacles between him and the career he has always known he wanted. In early 2009, he enrolled in Atlanta's Sound Audio Engineering (SAE) Institute, a one-year program where he'll get the required training in his chosen profession. "Once I graduate I'll be ready to get started in the music business," he says. "I'll be the guy in the studio with the headphones on, recording, editing, and producing the music."

And back in Atlanta, Parker will be able to continue doing what he's made a point of since his injury: going back to Shepherd to visit other ABI patients, to tell them he knows what they're going through—"because I'm the only one they can talk to who really knows."

Betty is there every week, in her volunteer work with Family Support Services, and the help she gives to patients' families—sometimes counseling, sometimes just listening, sometimes sharing Parker's story—is no less valuable. But she admits she can't offer what Parker offers. "It's

Parker with his parents, Betty and Rob, and their three family dogs.

amazing to watch Parker and another patient," she says, "because you can see the connection. The other patients look right into Parker's eyes, as though asking him to tell them the words they need to hear, to help get them through." Parker agrees: "When I look in their eyes, I can tell where they are."

Both mother and son are happy to give back. "I say all the time, Shepherd gave Parker his life back," Betty declares. "It's not just that the people are top-notch; it's also the attitude—I can't stress how important that is. When you are a patient, or patient's family—that positive energy all around you just feeds you, makes you want to do better."

"Of course, it helps," adds Parker, "that the people there knew exactly what to do, when to do it, how much to do. And when something doesn't work, they figure out a different way. They are not just caring, but also creative and spontaneous in the way they go about their work."

Now Parker King, creative, spontaneous, and again brimming with a young man's energy, is ready to go about his work.

SHE COULD WRITE A BOOK

"**W**ow!"
THAT'S HOW NATALIE
RODRIGUEZ SUMS UP HER RESPONSE WHEN
SHE FOUND OUT—long after the fact—what happened to her on the
night of January 18, 2004. "It was unbelievable to sit there listening to what happened to me," she says today. "I'm just blessed to be alive, and I thank the Lord for
that every day."

Natalie was 15 at the time, excited about having made the freshman
basketball team at her high school in Nashville, Tennessee, and otherwise
engaged in the fine life of a teenager—"hanging out with my friends, having a good time. But also," she hastens to add, "a very good student."

Natalie was watching a football game with her father that
Sunday evening when her girlfriends called to tell her to come on over.
Her sister dropped her off. She and her friends got in a car. Her life
resumed, insofar as she was conscious of it, many months later.

Natalie's mother, Susie, had left the house that night to run some
errands. The next day was a school holiday, and Susie expected that
Natalie and her sister would be hanging out with their friends that
night. She didn't expect the call she got on her cell phone, from a
neighbor who had just received word: "There had been a horrific accident on Rutland Road, just a half-mile away from our house."

Five years later, some of the details remain puzzling. "The girls
had left their purses and stuff at the house where Natalie had gone to
visit," says Susie. "Some of them even had their pajamas on. So it wasn't like
they were really going out somewhere. But apparently someone came over,
and they all piled in the car." Susie does know that the girls were on a dark road
on a dark, cold, misty night, that the girl driving lost control of the car and hit
a tree head-on. Natalie, riding behind the driver, was
thrown forward and smashed
against

the windshield. More critically injured than any of the other girls, she was "life-flighted" to Vanderbilt University Medical Center.

From that point on, says Susie, "It was a nightmare." First there was the long wait for information, the terrible uncertainty. "The first communication we had was from a social worker at the facility, who said she needed to see the parents of all the 'victims.' So we all went to the trauma unit on the 10th floor and waited some more. It was at least another hour before I was allowed to see Natalie for the first time." At last Susie was approached by Dr. Morris, the attending physician that night, who described the extent of Natalie's injuries. The most life-threatening, the doctor believed, was traumatic brain injury, with swelling, but there were a host of other severe injuries: internal bleeding, a crushed femur, broken ribs, and fractured chin and jaw

The situation remained critical throughout the night, recalls Susie, and at the 7:00 A.M. update, they learned that Natalie's condition was continuing to deteriorate. The brain was still swelling; she was breathing only thanks to a ventilator. The doctors decided to use Phenobarbital to induce a coma, then try to drain the fluid that was increasing the pressure on her brain. "Thankfully," says Susie, "they did not have to operate to remove any part of her brain."

Then it seemed Natalie's heart could take no more. On the third day she went into cardiac arrest but was quickly resuscitated. "On the fifth day," says Susie, "she went into total cardiac arrest. They 'coded' her. Basically, they said she was gone." Some seconds later, she began breathing again, but the doctors still felt the battle had been lost. "They wanted my authorization for an emergency CT scan, just to provide us with a 'final report.' They also wanted to talk about organ donation." The results of the CT scan indicated that there was still blood flowing to the brain, recalls Susie, "but they were still asking about organ donation, and about whether we wanted to 'disconnect.' Of course, we said no. We couldn't disconnect because there was that blood flowing—there was life."

That's the way it went for almost three weeks, says Susie. "Chaotic, terrible, with all the fear and helplessness of watching your baby leave you. Every day was critical. Every day something else that might be the final blow." Only after 20 days was Natalie stable enough for the medical team to think about surgery to repair the badly broken leg. "And this was long surgery," Susie recalls, "five hours or so, with all the risks of anesthesia."

But Natalie hung on—and apparently convinced her doctors that she intended to keep hanging on. Now they "monitored her condition continually," says Susie, awaiting the time when Natalie would be stable enough to be transferred to a rehabilitation facility. Then, on her 26th day at Vanderbilt, Natalie opened one eye. "It was a blank look," says Susie. "No emotion, only an occasional tear. But it was something."

Meanwhile, a therapist with Natalie's case management team at Vanderbilt had raised the question of where Natalie might go for rehab. "It was a huge decision," says Susie, "and since we had never been in such a situation, it was all very confusing." Proximity to Nashville was certainly an important factor, and Shepherd met that criteria.

Once Shepherd was under consideration, the Rodriguezes studied videos of the hospital and then spoke in person to a Tennessee-based admission liaison. "We discovered that Shepherd Center met Natalie's needs, and ours," says Susie. "They assured us that Natalie would have a private room during her rehabilitation, and that was important. And it was also very important that

Natalie with her mother, Susie, and her sister, Paula.

I have a place to stay, and Shepherd could offer that, too. Even though we still didn't know what Natalie's outcome would be, we felt comfortable going to a facility that had so much to offer."

Nevertheless, says Susie, arrival at Shepherd in February was overwhelming. "Just seeing the name, 'catastrophic hospital'—that's when the reality of what had happened really hit me." She credits the Shepherd staff—Dr. Leslie and Natalie's therapy team—with easing her misgivings. She was thoroughly informed as to "the whole plan of care," and she was assured that she would be constantly updated on Natalie's progress.

Still, it was a difficult time, all the more so because only Susie could be away from Nashville to watch over Natalie's rehab. "At first she was still unconscious," Susie recalls, "and then there were several surgeries she had to undergo at Piedmont. She was in pain, she was exhausted, her mouth was wired shut from the fracture of her jaw. It was a lot to deal with." And all the while the therapy continued—the hard work to get Natalie up and into a wheelchair. "That was huge," says Susie.

Susie was by Natalie's side at Shepherd for 30 days, the normal length of inpatient rehabilitation. But Natalie needed more. "They approached me about extending Natalie's stay," says Susie, "and they were able to get approval from the insurance, so we continued her therapy." Susie got a hotel room and brought her mother down to Atlanta. Her mother's presence at the hospital allowed Susie to return to Nashville for the workweek and then come back to Shepherd on the weekends.

The painstaking work continued—physical, speech, and occupational therapy—and Natalie continued to progress, slowly. Then, at last, a breakthrough: "After 64 days at Shepherd," says Susie, "Natalie spoke for the first time. I was at work and got a call from my mother and from Jennifer, the speech therapist; they put Natalie on the phone and Natalie said, 'Mommy.' The minute we got off work, we jumped in the car and raced back down to Atlanta."

After 64 days at Shepherd, Natalie spoke for the first time. I was at work and got a call from my mother and from Jennifer, the speech therapist; they put Natalie on the phone and Natalie said, "Mommy."

—Susie Rodriguez

On May 1, after close to three months of rehab, Natalie was discharged. "She had a wheelchair," says Susie, "but Natalie has always been stubborn. She wanted to walk out of there. So, slowly, she left the facility on her feet, walking. That was a blessing."

The Rodriguez family was ready to go home, so instead of entering Natalie in Pathways, Shepherd helped arrange for Natalie to receive outpatient rehabilitation at Vanderbilt University Medical Center. "We started with four days a week," says Susie. "She still had quite a way to go. It was hard for her to stay focused. Her speech was still confused. And emotionally, well, she would get upset."

In all, Natalie would spend a year and a half in outpatient rehab at Vanderbilt—gradually reducing the number of days per week there. Even those months, she says, are a "big blur," and she has no memory at all of her time at Shepherd. "But we took lots of videos and photographs," says Susie, "so Natalie can have some idea of what she went through during all those months. We wanted a lot of documentation, because it was an amazing thing for all of us." The family also returned to Shepherd, about a year after her discharge. "Natalie wanted to see it, wanted to see the staff and Dr. Leslie, so she could connect the real thing to the pictures we had. It was part of her life."

Thanks to almost two years of hard work, at Shepherd and at Vanderbilt, that life has been restored. "It took a long time to get her going again," says Susie, "to get her back to herself. I remember that first Christmas after the completion of her therapy—she was really happy." She was also hitting the books, a process that began during her rehab at Vanderbilt and culminated, remarkably, when she rejoined her class during the second semester of her junior year. "It was really exhausting at first," she recalls. "I couldn't tolerate the whole eight-hour day and would come home at noon." But she hung in, kept up, made it through the rest of that year and then graduated on schedule with her class in the spring of 2006—"with a very good grade point average," she's quick to add.

The next fall Natalie enrolled at Nashville State and spent a year and a half there with the idea of pursuing a nursing degree. "Eventually," she says, "I realized that wasn't for me, so now

Natalie with her mother, Susie, her sister Paula, and her father, Danny.

I'm taking some time to figure out what I want to do." In the meantime, when she's not working part-time, she writes. "Stuff just pours into my mind, and I write it down," she says. It's a talent she cultivated as a member of the staff of her high school newspaper. "I wrote a lot of really good articles for the paper," she says, and Susie confirms that Natalie has always been creative.

One thing's for sure: what Natalie has been through would make a heck of a book. But whether she turns her energy to that kind of endeavor is irrelevant. All that's important is that the energy is there. "I'm in good spirits," she declares. "I don't let anything hold me down. What I went through only made me stronger."

Dollars and Sensitivity

Here's the standard script: Not-for-profit institution is founded by naive dreamers with more vision than experience. Against all odds, institution succeeds, grows by leaps and bounds, becomes complex corporate entity in need of pragmatic financial leadership. Hires tough-minded chief financial officer to crack whip on idealists and do-gooders—and tolls death knell for culture of family-run enterprise.

But Shepherd CFO Steve Holleman, who had worked at for-profit hospitals in Texas and Atlanta before coming to Shepherd Center in 1995, was well aware that the Shepherd story followed a different script. Which suited him just fine. "Every time my wife and I would drive down Peachtree," says Holleman, "we could see that something special, something unique was going on here. The more I found out, the more it seemed like there was this little jewel in the middle of the city. I was very fortunate that the opening came along and I got hired."

Actually, part of the standard script did apply. When Holleman was hired as director of financial Services, Jason Shelnutt was both the CFO and the chief operating officer (COO). But the hospital was growing so fast, it became impossible for any one person to hold both those jobs, so the CFO title was passed to Holleman in 1997. Growth has only accelerated since then. Holleman estimates the 2008–2009 operating budget to be about $120 million a year—twice what it was just a few years ago. The hospital also has about $275 million in assets, a number that has tripled since his arrival and that also, says Holleman, "makes us a pretty substantial-sized organization." That figure includes Shepherd's close to $50 million endowment, an asset that has grown astronomically over the last decade, in large part because of the success of the 25th anniversary campaign, which generated $56.2 million in private support.

In fact, says Holleman, Shepherd's generous donors constitute an important revenue stream, dependably contributing some $10 million to $15 million a year. Another $5 million comes from grants and research contracts. "But the vast majority of revenue comes from in-patient care, from services provided to patients, and then, to a lesser extent, from out-patient and day programs. And now taking on increased emphasis is investment income—at least under normal circumstances."

Elaborating on the economic meltdown, Holleman notes that one of the hospital's pressing financial challenges right now is to recover from the market losses incurred since April 2008. "We've been beat to hell," he says. "We're still strong, but not as strong, and one of my jobs is to recoup that." It won't be easy or quick, says Holleman, because the recovery must come without any compromise in the quality of patient care.

That's where the script begins to get rewritten. "Here at Shepherd," says Holleman, "I've been able to develop the philosophy that if we do good work, the money will flow from that. The patient comes first, and second, and third. If we do all the right things by the patients and their families, maintain our emphasis on quality care and customer service, and keep an eye on the dollars, the hospital will be okay." As for the old script, says Holleman, "The for-profit healthcare world is a different animal altogether. The mission is just not there, at least where I worked. That's what makes Shepherd so great: we are focused on the patient. And I tell people that if we ever get to where we're focused more on the dollars than on the patients, we might as well shut the doors—because that's not what Shepherd Center is about."

In other words, quality first—which, when you think about it, is not all that radical a proposition. "Finally," explains Holleman, "it's our quality that makes everything else possible. We can market ourselves successfully, and we can develop relationships with payers who care about outcomes. That brings patients in. Also, if we're providing the best outcome, doing great research, and giving great service, the donor community will support us. If we stay focused on the right things, we don't have to focus on the money."

Rather than the stern taskmaster who goes around scowling at those who would upset his balance sheet, Holleman sees himself as a facilitator of the "real" work that goes on at Shepherd. "We try not to use the word 'miracle' loosely around here," he says. "After all, some of the folks that come here are fortunate enough to regain a lot of function, and some aren't. But I'll tell you what: patients' families sometimes throw that word out there—when they see where they've ended up compared to where they thought they would be. They've been in the therapy gyms and watched those people work; they've seen what can happen. To me the nurses and therapists are the real heroes around here—getting down on the floor with these people, pushing them to stay with it and not give up. I'm just happy to play my role and give whatever support I can."

Steve Holleman, Chief Financial Officer.

Nevertheless, Holleman laughs when he hears James Shepherd refer to him as "a financial guy with a heart." "I get the oxymoron," he says, "but, actually, this is a very easy place to have a heart. That comes from James and Alana and Harold, and the rest of the board. Not to mention the whole atmosphere around here. All you have to do is walk around and find two or three patients who have a better attitude than you do on a given day, and it'll fix your perspective real quick. It humbles you, really."

Here's Holleman's version of the Shepherd script: "What the Shepherds have created here is truly remarkable. It's very much a family-driven, heart-driven, mission-driven business, even though, at this point in time, we've grown way beyond the mom-and-pop profile. We provide the broadest continuum, we think we provide as much if not more research, we try to achieve outcomes that are better than anybody else's. That is, we try to do a lot. Our joke here is that we're small but we're complicated. It's challenging, but also very rewarding, and our relatively small size helps us hang onto that sense of intimacy."

And far from squashing Shepherd's unique culture under the boot-heel of some black-ink imperative, Holleman cherishes it as much as anybody. "The culture here makes all the difference," he says, and he also asserts that keeping that spirit alive is a fundamental priority. "Our founders and pioneers, our career Shepherd people, aren't going to be around forever," he says, "and instilling that culture for the next generation is one of the things we're working on the hardest right now."

WINDING ROAD TO RECOVERY

ᘓᘻ

$\mathcal{D}$AVE AND MEAGHAN LONG MET 15 YEARS AGO IN A POLICE DEPART-
MENT in Columbus, Ohio, where he was an officer and she was a dis-
patcher. Dave's uncle, also a Columbus police officer, had steered him toward
the academy, but police work had never been Dave's first career choice. He
had joined the Army Reserves upon graduating from high school, and the
life of a U.S. serviceman still beckoned. He enlisted for active duty in July
1996, and Meaghan prepared for the role of Army wife. Neither could
have guessed what lay in store.

After three years at Fort Stewart, Georgia, Dave was assigned to
Fort Belvoir, right outside of Washington, D.C., in July 1999. His unit
was stationed at the Pentagon on September 11, 2001. "I was on duty
when the plane hit the building," recalls Dave, "but not exactly at the
Pentagon. We were across the street at Fort Myers." His unit had to
"wait for the red tape to be cut," and didn't get deployed to the Pentagon until about four o'clock in the afternoon. "First thing I remember everybody saying was that it looked just like the Oklahoma
City bombing, a scene like that, all the smoke and debris." Most of the
soldiers in his unit had been through Emergency Medical Technician
(EMT) school, so at first they were sent in for "search and rescue." But
after the medics and firefighters arrived on the scene, says Dave, "our mission became just search and recovery." Casualties at the Pentagon that day
numbered a hundred twenty-five.

Dave and Meaghan shipped out for Hawaii in July 2002. By the following spring, the United States was at war in Iraq, and Dave's engineer unit
was sent into action in January 2004. Their mission was "heavy lifting"—
clearing or upgrading roads, airfields, and pipelines, and
other big construction projects of
that nature.

On June 16, 2004, Dave and some fellow soldiers were walking around outside the Post Exchange (PX) at their installation in Balad, 50 miles north of Bagdad. "It was supposed to be a safe zone, but mortar fire had been coming in pretty much every day. We caught one, a big one. When the shell exploded, I saw the guy to my left get hit in the face, and both he and a guy on my right were killed." Dave lost consciousness, then awoke to find bodies lying everywhere. He's not sure of the number of casualties—at least a dozen, some of them civilians.

He wasn't fully aware of what had happened, but knew enough to try to take cover, so he walked into the lobby of the PX, the nearest building. He remembers the destruction, the broken glass all over the place, but, probably because of the adrenaline, his own body seemed okay, so he figured the thing to do was to try to start walking back to his unit. "The medics were telling me to take a knee, and I'm saying, 'What are you talking about? There's nothing wrong with me.' But then I realized there was blood coming from my ear." Dave explains that when the medics see an injured person, they've immediately got to strip all his clothes off to see the extent of the damage. But he couldn't understand why they were doing that to him. He still was convinced that he had no serious injury. The next thing he knew, though, he was being lowered on a stretcher, loaded onto a Humvee, and taken to the nearby military hospital. Dave remembers the scene there: "You could hear the choppers coming in with new patients, taking others out. It was total chaos."

The only physical sensation he recalls feeling at this point was some shortness of breath, which he attributed to all the excitement. But suddenly he realized that there was a "full-bird colonel" shaving his chest. "I was like, 'Sir, what are you doing?' He told me he was prepping me for emergency surgery, and I say, 'What for?' That's when I got the news." The doctor told Dave that he had a class-3 laceration of his liver, meaning that shrapnel had pretty much cut his liver in half, and that he needed immediate surgery to repair the liver and remove all the other shrapnel in his body. Dave says he awoke from the anesthesia to find that "they had basically cut me from the sternum down to the pelvic bone. Then, as soon as they figured I was ready, they were going to medevac me out of the theater."

Meaghan was back in Ohio when the call came through. She wanted to be home with family during Dave's deployment. "I was on the phone with my mom," she recalls, "and saw that it was a military number from Hawaii." With her husband in Iraq, she couldn't imagine why anybody would be calling from Hawaii, but she clicked onto the line to find out. "This man asked me for my maiden name, and I laughed because it had been so long since I had called myself that. Then he said, 'This is Lt. Col. Fly from Casualty Affairs,' and my heart hit the floor." The man could tell Meaghan only that Dave had been at the installation where there had been a major explosion that that he was in critical condition. If the situation warranted it, he would call back the next day to talk about flying her out. "My mom is a nurse," says Meaghan, "and she and I both understood that it was bad."

She made arrangements for the care of the two children, and sure enough, the call came the next morning. "They wanted to know how soon I could get on a plane." The plan was to fly her to the Army hospital in Germany where Dave was now in the intensive care unit. But Meaghan didn't have a passport, and getting one would have held her up in Washington for two days. So, instead, she was sent directly to Walter Reed, to await Dave's arrival there—which turned out not to be the most logical option. "It was horrible," says Meaghan. "I ended up waiting at Walter Reed for four days, while they made sure he was stable enough to make that journey. He was in the ICU in Germany for five days."

Dave was "pretty much out of it" during those five days in Germany. At Walter Reed, though, the story of his injury began to take an interesting turn. He recalls that the hospital hosted "an event" for the patients shortly after he arrived, and he was trying to get all fixed up for the affair. "I keep my head shaved," he says, "and I was having Meaghan do the honors. She asked me to turn my head to the right, and I turned it to the left. She tried again: 'Dave, turn your head to the right.' I said, 'I am turning it to the right.'"

There were other "small indicators"—for example, the way Dave's left eye would blink a little bit after his right eye. But no medical personnel, either in Germany or at Walter Reed, had broached the subject of brain injury. "I guess they were just focused on the liver injury," says Dave. He was at Walter Reed for about three weeks and then sent home for 30 days of convalescent leave—"with Meaghan changing the bandages every day." Back at Walter Reed, Dave finally got into neural-psych testing—"thanks to the persistence of my wife and her mom, who kept noticing all these symptoms while I was home."

While still awaiting his test results, Dave got orders to return to Hawaii. Then, just eight months after his injury, it was back to Iraq. "The neural-psych tests came back 'inconclusive,'" says Dave, "and my body had healed up pretty well, so I was cleared to head out for another tour with my battalion."

During his second deployment, Dave knew he was "having issues" but thought he might simply be suffering from post-traumatic stress disorder. The medical staff—which at this installation consisted of "a bunch of Navy doctors"—was no help. "All they wanted to do was medicate me, but, on the other hand, you're not supposed to be medicated in a combat zone. So I just had to deal, and fortunately, nothing major went wrong."

Back stateside, and now a squad leader, Dave was required to enroll in the basic noncommissioned officer course, or B-NOC, the basic non-commissioned officer course. Here the real extent of Dave's injury had a chance to manifest itself. The course was "reference-oriented," as Dave explains. The tests were open-book, with all the material right there on the computer—no memorization necessary. "Even still I almost didn't pass. I just wasn't comprehending the material like I used to be able to." Next thing he knew, he got orders to report to Fort Jackson, South Carolina, to be a drill instructor. "Meaghan was concerned," he says, "but it was either that or be deployed for a third time."

"I was more than concerned," says Meaghan. "It was obvious when he came back home from his second tour that things had gone downhill." During his two weeks of B-NOC, "he was freaking out. I would sit down and go over the material with him, and it was obvious that it was just not registering." Meaghan's mother, who was visiting at the time, put it bluntly: "Meaghan, he's getting worse."

At Fort Jackson, in the summer of 2007, Dave entered what he calls his "dazed and confused" period. He had headaches, chest pains, dizziness; he couldn't concentrate on his work. "When there was a lot of stuff going on," he says, "I would just have a brain freeze. Basically I had a meltdown." The doctors on the base were used to dealing with the trainees, not with combat-related injuries. Out of options and out of patience, Meaghan called the Wounded Warriors hotline.

"I saw no help coming from the medical staff on the base," says Meaghan, "so I pretty much took over at that point, in terms of trying to get him the attention that he needed." Created in response to the widely publicized problems with veterans' care at Walter Reed, the hotline promises swift action, and Dave and Meaghan were quickly contacted by a nurse case manager at the base hospital. "Her name was Susan Manczuk," says Meaghan, "and she was absolutely the nicest person in the world. She made sure that Dave got what he needed."

Not that it was easy. Susan successfully battled to have Dave admitted to the VA hospital in Augusta, Georgia, for three months of evaluation, but the doctors there were still unwilling to conclude that Dave's symptoms were not ultimately posttraumatic stress distorder (PTSD) related. Finally, toward the end of his stay, he underwent some vision tests that revealed some "deficits"—some impairment, some irregularity. "They couldn't explain why," says Dave. The upshot was that, back at Fort Jackson, Dave was put on a regimen of vision therapy—nothing more.

"Susan came through again," says Meaghan—by putting Dave and Meaghan in touch with the deputy director of the hospital, an eye specialist who, as it happened, had recently been invited to Atlanta to tour Shepherd Center. During his visit he learned about Shepherd's new SHARE Initiative and, aware of Dave's unusual vision problems, thought Dave might be a candidate for the program. "When he came back and told us this might be right for Dave," says Meaghan, "we were super excited. Finally, it looked like he would get what he needed."

Meaghan says they knew they were in the right place after Dave had been put through another round of neural-psych testing. This would be Dave's third such evaluation, and at first Meaghan and Dave worried that it would be another exercise in futility. But the therapist reassured them: "She told us that if this test didn't give us a conclusive diagnosis, she would find one that did. 'We'll figure this thing out,' she said, and that's exactly what they did." Ultimately, tests revealed brain injury specifically linked to Dave's dizziness, and Shepherd physiatrist Dr. Rhonda Taubin offered a definite diagnosis of ABI rather than PTSD. "It was really amazing to me," says Meaghan, "because nobody else had taken the time to look outside of the box and really find the problem."

Shortly thereafter, Dave was signed up for four weeks of therapy at Pathways, Shepherd's outpatient program for brain injury patients. The military arranged for him to fly from Columbia to Atlanta on Sunday evenings and then back on Thursday evenings to be home with Meaghan on the weekends. "I made remarkable progress, especially in memory and reading comprehension," says Dave. "I'm also doing physical therapy—balance exercises—to repair the vestibular part of the brain that was causing my dizziness. The therapist told me that it would be an ongoing process—that I would have to keep working at it on my own, and I'm doing it." Adds Meaghan, "The progress he made at Shepherd was incredible. His case manager, Kendra Moon, and I were either e-mailing or on the phone pretty constantly. She told me everything that was going on—which was a very different experience."

Dave is back at Fort Jackson now, still in contact with Shepherd therapists when the need arises, and still getting better. He applied to the "medical reclassification board," which found him

Dave with his wife Meaghan, daughter, Abbey, and son, Aidan.

"fit for duty" and granted him permission to change his military occupation. He has applied to be a 42 Alpha, an administrative specialist, which requires that he make it through phase-two B-NOC and then A-NOC (the advanced noncommissioned officer course). But Dave is sure he can handle the work now.

Plus, the timing is right. Meaghan, too, is in school, studying for a degree in nursing. Dave figures she has another year and a half, by which time he will have completed his advanced training and been promoted to E-7. Beyond that, eight more years will get him to 20, and a pretty nice retirement pension. But Dave's goal is not retirement. It's to make Sergeant major.

That's fine with Meaghan, now that Dave is finally on the mend. "It's funny. When Dave survived that explosion in 2004, we were so grateful that he was given a second chance." But it wasn't quite that simple. Dave and Meaghan had to endure four difficult, frustrating years. "Now," says Meagan, "thanks to Shepherd and to Dr. Taubin, we are finally getting that second chance."

Terran Cooper, SHARE Initiative Coordinator.

SHARE-ing THE SACRIFICE

Everybody agrees that credit for the SHARE (Shaping Hope and Recovery Excellence) Initiative goes to longtime Shepherd benefactor Bernie Marcus. As Susan Johnson tells it, "When the media began reporting on the inadequate care being given to soldiers returning from Iraq and Afghanistan with brain and/or spinal cord injury, Mr. Marcus approached Dr. Leslie, along with James and Alana Shepherd, to talk about ways to get these soldiers the care they needed." Or, in Dr. Leslie's words, "Bernie called up and said, 'We've got to do something about these soldiers.'"

Marcus was willing to provide the funding, and Shepherd certainly had the rehabilitation expertise. One problem, though, says Johnson, was that "the VA was reluctant to give up the patients, since doing so would be seen as an admission of inadequacy." So Mitch Fillhaber, Shepherd's vice president of Marketing and Managed Care, went directly to Humana Military Healthcare Services and TRICARE, the benefits administrator, and, according to Johnson, "they were thrilled to join us in a collaborative relationship."

As a result, in January 2008 Shepherd Center launched another innovative program, extending yet farther its mission to provide catastrophic care to populations in need of its world-renowned medical and rehabilitation expertise. Officially a partnership between Marcus, Shepherd Center, and Humana Military Healthcare Services, the SHARE Initiative allows Shepherd to provide medical rehabilitation, postacute rehabilitation, and community and family support services that might fall outside of coverage under TRICARE, the organization that administers health benefits for members of the military and their dependents.

While the program serves soldiers who have suffered either spinal cord or brain injury, Dr. Leslie believes that most of the cases at Shepherd will involve traumatic brain injury (TBI), since the Army estimates that 10 to 20 percent of troops leaving Iraq and Afghanistan have signs of concussion, or mild traumatic brain injury—often called "the signature wound" of the war. According to Terran Cooper, the program's coordinator, as of early 2009 SHARE had already provided care to more than 100 current and former service members, "and we're serving 10 to 15 of these people at any given time." In fact, developing the program was at first only a part-time assignment for Cooper, but, she says, "it was immediately apparent that it was more than a part-time job. Now we have a dedicated, postacute brain injury SHARE team, a brain injury team that deals only with service members. "

Some of these soldiers appeared to be falling through the cracks of the military bureaucracy and were not getting what their families had thought they should get, or the outcome they had hoped for.

— DR. DONALD LESLIE

Symptoms can include problems with memory, attention, concentration and sleeping, as well as headaches, confusion, dizziness, nausea and irritability. As Dave Long's story dramatically illustrates, posttraumatic stress disorder is also often associated with such symptoms, which can make diagnosis more difficult. That's why the program's services include neuropsychological evaluation to confirm TBI—along with cognitive therapy, counseling, activity- and community-based rehabilitation, residential services and respite care for family members, and housing while services are being delivered.

Describing the unique challenge facing the SHARE Initiative, Cooper calls the service men and women in the program Shepherd's "new treatment" population. "Their military service, particularly in the many instances when they were injured in a combat situation, added a whole new dimension for us." Expanding on the point, she explains that in many of these cases providing medical care is just the first part of the problem; the second, and equally essential, part is return to the community—"which is why we are so fortunate to have the Marcus Community Bridge Program."

What makes the return to the community such a complicated piece of the puzzle is the fact that, for many of these people, the military was the community. "If I were catastrophically injured," says Cooper, "I would probably be able to return to my same home. I would still have my same spouse and child, and, very likely, I would return to my same job here at Shepherd. But not so for these young men who have been in active duty. Being in the service has been their job. It has been their home. And if they cannot go back to that, their whole world has evaporated. Everything has changed—job, home, daily life, financial status, and often even family—everything."

The SHARE Initiative is a unique program, but it pushes Shepherd Center into familiar waters—extending care beyond that which the medical insurance bureaucracy—in this case the military medical insurance bureaucracy—deems necessary. As Dr. Leslie puts it, "What Bernie was responding to was that some of these soldiers appeared to be falling through the cracks of the military bureaucracy and were not getting what their families had thought they should get, or the outcome they had hoped for." Trying to solve the problem, of course, "risks stepping on the toes of the Pentagon and the VA," he continues, "and you don't want to do that. They are doing what they can, and our job is to be a partner, not an adversary."

"Absolutely," confirms Cooper. "We work very hard to make sure we are being recognized as a friend, not a foe. Our position is this: we are going to continue to reach out and offer support, but we are not going to bash you about it."

Still, the mission is tricky, especially as the program increasingly seeks to help veterans, the very people who need SHARE the most. "The real problem," says Cooper, "comes when these veterans, now separated from the military, who may or may not have been identified as brain injured, find themselves in the world of the VA, which isn't prepared to meet their needs. Now you have a high potential for a vicious cycle of chronic pain, narcotic medications, sleep disruption, and family dysfunction, along with vocational, legal, and financial difficulties."

Cooper understands and sympathizes with the position of the VA. In the first place, she says, "It's a case of not knowing what you don't know, of how difficult it is to have insight into your own system." Beyond that, there are still residual effects from the Walter Reed scandal. "They remain fearful of media bashing, understandably," says Cooper. "There's the feeling that if they acknowledge a weakness, they make themselves more vulnerable."

The good news is that, slowly, the situation is changing. Cooper says Shepherd has "the extreme good fortune" of a productive relationship with the director of the Atlanta VA. And, more generally, "as more of these individuals come into the system, the VA is beginning to see what we have been trying to describe. They are more receptive to making referrals to us and more interested in our thoughts and feedback."

Dr. Leslie, too, notes that "it is happening. Our partners are realizing that we are good at what we do—evaluating these people, determining what their needs are, and figuring out how to meet those needs." But at the same time he emphasizes the urgency of the situation. "So many soldiers have been deployed, again and again, and over time have been exposed to these blast injuries—posttraumatic headaches, blackouts, memory deficits, higher-level cognitive issues—and the more you scratch the surface the deeper it gets. It's just a huge issue, and one that isn't going away any time soon, what with Iraq and now Afghanistan."

Typically, Shepherd is there. Typically, Shepherd's good work is made possible by the incredible generosity of its donor community. "We have been unbelievably fortunate to have Mr. Marcus take this on as a heartfelt mission," says Cooper, "and to allow us to develop this program. Because of the potential size of the problem we are trying to alleviate, it is incumbent upon us not only to provide care for these people, but maybe even more important, to spread our wealth of expertise into any entity—military or VA—who will accept our help, so they can ramp up to meet this population's needs."

How? "It's a grassroots effort," says Cooper. "We go to groups like the Wounded Warrior Regiment of the Marine Corps and say, 'Here's who we are and what we're doing. If you have someone who you think could benefit from our evaluation and intervention, call us.' My associate, Nancy Philips, and I are out there spreading the word, finding the right organizations and the right people." Cooper adds that finding those people "and helping them get their lives back on track is an incredible experience."

Dr. Ben Thrower, Medical Director, Multiple Sclerosis Institute

THE ANDREW C. CARLOS MULTIPLE SCLEROSIS INSTITUTE

When Shepherd found Dr. Ben Thrower, he had wandered a long way from home. A South Carolina native and graduate of the medical school at the University of Florida, Dr. Thrower found himself practicing medicine in the opposite corner of the country—Spokane, Washington. Not that he was complaining. He had been named medical director of the Multiple Sclerosis Institute at Holy Family Hospital, one of the nonprofit Catholic hospitals in the area.

It was a good situation. In the first place, there was need. In the northern United States., as in northern Europe, there is a relatively high incidence of multiple sclerosis (MS). Although nowadays MS "has less respect for geography," Dr. Thrower theorizes that "the genetic component of the disease originated in the British Isles and went on up." It may be, he says, a matter of vitamin D: "The further from the equator, the less sunlight, and with that change in vitamin D metabolism, more MS." Consequently, even before he took the job at Holy Family, Dr. Thrower found that 60 percent of his neurology practice consisted of MS patients.

In the second place, Holy Family was dedicated to "the comprehensive model" of MS treatment. "They understood that you have to have physical therapy (PT) and occupational therapy (OT) and the whole program if you want to do it right, and they wanted to do it right." And finally there was the fact that Spokane is not a terrible place to live. The Air Force, to which his wife owed a stint of service, could have sent the young couple anywhere. When she got her assignment in Spokane, says Dr. Thrower, "we were thrilled. We knew there was civilization there."

There was only one problem. "It wasn't home for either one of us. We kept watching for something in the Southeast—where the children would have grandparents." Then one day Dr. Thrower got a phone call from June Halpern, with the consortium of MS centers, letting him know that the position of medical director for MS at Shepherd Center had opened up. "She also said that Shepherd was a great place that had every-

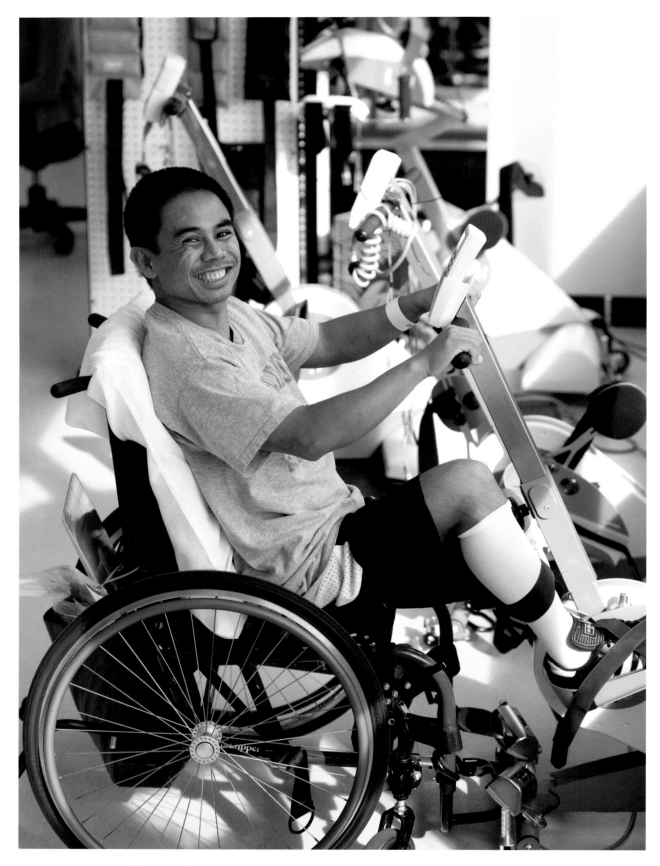

Marc Floresca, of West Memphis, AR, uses the functional electrical stimulation (FES) bicycle.

thing I was looking for." He came for an interview in 2001 and joined Shepherd's medical staff in June of that year.

What really lured him, says Dr. Thrower, was the Shepherd family and their philosophy of patient care. "There's one thing that anybody who works with MS understands and is committed to," says Dr. Thrower. "You need the time to do what you need to do. You cannot push people through on an assembly line. I made it clear when I was interviewing that we would need a certain amount of time for every initial appointment, a certain amount of time for every follow-up, and nobody ever blinked." In fact, says Dr. Thrower, it is the opportunity to build long-term relationships with patients that drew him to MS. "It used to be that people were attracted to neurology because of the detective work—to figure out the mysteries of Alzheimer's or Parkinson's, even when there was really no treatment." With MS, there's still plenty of detective work, "but now we've got a lot more treatment to offer people. And that therapeutic work is what really excites me."

What really lured him, says Dr. Thrower, was the Shepherd family and their philosophy of patient care. And it is the opportunity to build long-term relationships with patients that drew him to MS... "that therapeutic work is what really excites me."

Dr. Thrower also has plenty of people to treat, since the MS program (officially known as the Andrew C. Carlos MS Institute as of 2003) has grown by a staggering amount since its inception 16 years ago. According to Emily Cade, MS case manager, Shepherd, as of 2010, is treating close to 3,000 MS patients. "It's a very large program," says Cade, "and thanks to the complete line of services we offer—including medical management through our neurologists, IV infusion suites on site, and MS rehab—we're a one-stop-shop."

So what is multiple sclerosis anyway? "Sclerosis," explains Dr. Thrower, "means 'hardening.'" It seems that back in 1868, Jean Charcot, "the father of modern neurology," noted symptoms like those ascribed to MS patients today—numbness or tingling, for example—and when he examined their brains postmortem, he discovered "these shiny white hardened areas, lots of them, so he named the disease multiple sclerosis, as in 'lots of hard places.'"

As for what it does, MS is a disease of the autoimmune system in which white blood cells, which are supposed to protect against illness, instead turn on the body and begin to destroy the myelin—the fatty insulation around nerve fibers that acts much like the insulation around electrical wires. "Myelin allows for very fast and efficient electrical conduction up and down the nerve fiber," says Dr. Thrower, "but if you strip that myelin away, which is what the inflammation with MS does, then you cannot conduct the information to and from the spinal cord." Moreover, Charcot theorized that MS could even "cut the wire" (sever the nerve fiber), but that theory was, says Dr. Thrower, "lost in translation." Then, just a decade ago, neurologist Bruce Trout confirmed Charcot's theory, showing definitively that MS could indeed "cut the wire." "That shook everybody up," says Dr. Thrower.

What causes the disease remains a mystery. "We know that there is some genetics and a little bit of environment, but outside of that there is much to learn," admits Dr. Thrower. "Also, how one person came to have MS is going to be different from the path that someone else took, so although there are some common themes, we are likely to find that there are many causes." As for those genetics, Dr. Thrower describes MS as "very weakly hereditary." If one of your parents had MS, your risk is about 2.5 percent. "That's a lot higher than the general population, but it's still very low. And overall, MS is still a very uncommon disease."

Adding to the mystery is "the wide spectrum over which MS can present," with cases ranging from benign to debilitating. "It's likely that some people have had the disease without ever knowing it," says Dr. Thrower; "in fact, the Mayo Clinic has argued that as much as 20 percent of the MS population might fall into that category." Dr. Thrower believes that estimate is high, but he notes that cases have been documented in which the disease has been detected via magnetic resonance imaging (MRI)—administered after a concussion, for example—before physical symptoms appear.

What's certain is that, because of the variety of ways by which it can present, it can be a very difficult disease to diagnose. According to the National MS Society, the average length of time from first symptoms to diagnosis is about three years. "That's not good," says Dr. Thrower, "because we know that the sooner we start treatment, the better the result." But MS refuses to cooperate by offering a standard manifestation. Sometimes symptoms are motor-related; sometimes they are sensory. "New numbness or tingling is really more common than weakness," says Dr. Thrower, "but that doesn't help much because those sensations can occur in pretty much any part of the body." Nor does it help that the number-one complaint has always been fatigue, because people who feel tired all the time "will get on the Internet and look up fatigue and end up with 300 different explanations."

Adding to the confusing array of symptoms is cognitive dysfunction—particularly memory loss. "Sometimes that's the first apparent symptom," says Dr. Thrower, "but it can occur at any stage, or not at all." In general, mild to moderate cognitive dysfunction can be seen in roughly 60 percent of the MS population, and in most of those cases patients realize that something's going on. "That's a blessing," says Dr. Thrower, "because if they are aware of it, they make us aware of it, and we can work on it." Of course, nothing's easy with MS. "Sometimes the fatigue and mood changes associated with MS wreak havoc on attention and concentration, which makes the cognition look much worse than it really is."

But Dr. Thrower is by no means daunted. At Shepherd he is marshaling an army of experts onto the battlefield. "We have such a great team here," he says, "including a second MD, Sherrill Loring, who joined us in 2008, two nurse practitioners, five RNs, three medical assistants, along with the whole cadre of physical therapists and occupational therapists—all part of our dedicated MS group. I feel very blessed to have all the resources available here." Emily Cade agrees: "Given how we've grown, I guess it would be possible to say we need more of this or that—like more space in our infusion suite—but we are incredibly lucky to have the facilities we have."

Then there is the research team—five research coordinators distinct from but working parallel to the clinical team. Dr. Thrower spends a third of his own time doing research—work that gets more exciting by the hour. "When I started here," he says, "the state of MS research was that if there was a decent-looking trial coming on, you got in on it. Now, there are really promising trials going on all the time. You have to pick and choose."

What researchers continue to move toward is "more effective drug therapy," says Dr. Thrower. A clear sign of progress is the fact that the "first line" of defense has expanded from the so-called "ABC" drugs (Avonex, Betaseron, and Copaxone) to include the recently developed Rebif. Just as the disease presents differently in different patients, so patients respond differently to the available therapies, which means it's good to have another weapon in the arsenal. "All four of these drugs," says Dr. Thrower, "have been proven effective, and they have all produced good safety data. Their weaknesses are that patients must give themselves an injection—never pleasant—and they don't completely stop the progression of MS for everybody."

So the search continues for something "both more effective and more convenient," which means, among other things, the development of "second line" drugs like the recently FDA-approved Tysabri. Unlike older chemotherapy medications that suppress the whole immune system (and therefore invite infection) Tysabri is a sort of "designer molecule created to hit a very specific target." Elaborating, Dr. Thrower explains that Tysabri "was designed to go in and block the ability for white blood cells to get into the brain and spinal cord in the first place" and that there are "a whole boat load of similar drugs now coming down the line—not only for MS, but for other diseases for well."

On the other hand, Tysabri and its companion drugs carry greater risk of potentially dangerous side effects, which is why, at least for now, they have been relegated to the "second line." In fact, says Dr. Thrower, Tysabri was withdrawn from the market temporarily "but has now been put back on, with the understanding that you probably wouldn't use it as your first choice. The recommendation is to try 'ABCR' first, then move to the second line if necessary."

If the disease is complicated, the approach is simple. "More research will produce improved therapies," says Dr. Thrower, "which is why our five research coordinators all carry at least three trials at any given time." The breakthrough on the immediate horizon is an oral medicine, which Dr. Thrower expects to be available this year. Then there are some "incredibly potent-looking drugs" in the pipeline—the "third line"—which will give patients with more aggressive MS another weapon in the arsenal. "Of course, the question will be, 'What's the risk-benefit ratio?'" says Dr. Thrower. "We're looking at one now called Campath, a once-a-year IV that looks to be incredibly effective but will it be too effective? The effect it has on certain white blood cells, even after that one course, can still be seen five years later. Will that invite infections later on?"

Beyond the "third line"? Beyond the development of the medication that stops the disease in its tracks? "Ah, then we get to start looking at the whole area of neural repair," says Dr. Thrower. "If we've stopped the progress of your disease, but you are already using a walker, our next goal would be to restore some of that function."

In other words, plenty remains to be done, and plenty remains to be learned, which suits both Dr. Thrower and Emily Cade just fine. As Cade says, "I've had some offers, but one of the best things about Shepherd is that I wake up every morning knowing I'm going to learn something new from the people I work with."

A POOL
BRIMMING OVER

❧

*I*T'S
SAFE TO SAY THAT NO-
BODY EVER WALKED THROUGH MORE
FAMILIAR DOORS THAN DID STEVE LORE when he came to
Shepherd as an MS patient in 2001. The courtly North Carolina native moved
to Atlanta in the early '80s, found a wife, Kay Sewell, found employment (at
Freeman & Hawkins, now Hawkins & Parnell), and, pretty soon thereafter,
found Shepherd Center. "It all started with Derby Day and the Junior Committee," says Steve, "back when we were young and happy-go-lucky. That's
what everybody did. My wife would put on the pretty hat and sundress,
and we'd go to Derby Day." Steve got a look inside the hospital when he
took one of the tours, and it confirmed his opinion that Shepherd was
a place where he might like to "hang around."

In fact, in 2001, when he needed a neurologist, about the only
thing Steve didn't know about Shepherd was that there was a very
fine one on the staff.

As Steve tells the story, he first noticed his symptoms while running. "I started tripping over tree roots and such, and I was working
harder and harder to keep up with my buddies. This was just not normal, and I didn't know why." His pals kidded him, told him he was getting lazy, but Steve knew something was wrong, so he walked across the
street to talk to his friend Walter James, a pulmonologist. Dr. James told
him, sensibly, to go see his internist, but the internist concluded that Steve
was just getting older, that he couldn't expect to run as fast as he once had.

"I went back to Walter," says Steve, "and after we talked about my symptoms some more, his opinion was that I might have a tumor either in my brain
or my spinal cord. He called a neurologist friend of his and told me he was setting me up for an MRI early the following week."

Steve's problem with that was that

he was

representing Eli Lilly at the time, during their Prozac litigation, and he absolutely had to be in Indianapolis all that next week. "I told him I couldn't do it that next week," says Steve, "but that I'd take care of it when I got back to town." That wasn't good enough for Dr. James, who persuaded his colleagues at Piedmont Hospital to let Steve come in for an MRI on Saturday.

"I went over to Walter's house after it was over," says Steve, "just to let him know I had followed his orders and that we would get the results in a week or so." But Dr. James's greeting was odd. "He told me to come on into his study, to let him get me a glass of lemonade. Lemonade? I knew something was up."

What was up was that the radiologist at Piedmont had e-mailed the MRI results to Dr. James. "I know what's wrong with you," said the doctor. Steve asked whether it was his brain or his spinal cord. "It's not a tumor," Dr. James told Steve, "but it's not good. You have multiple sclerosis.'"

Steve at first thought he might qualify as one of "Jerry's kids," until Dr. James clarified: no, it's not muscular dystrophy; it's multiple sclerosis. And Steve needed to see a neurologist immediately. "He told me to forget the trip to Indianapolis, that my spinal cord was badly swollen, and that if I didn't get it looked at as soon as possible, I might have problems more serious than tripping over tree roots."

Following his friend's advice, Steve got in to see a neurologist that Monday, an appointment that turned out better than Steve could have hoped. The physician prescribed the steroid Solu-Medrol, patted the patient on the back, and sent him home with a wonderful prognosis: "'Steve,' he told me, 'after you finish this prescription, you will never know that you have MS again as long as you live.' Needless to say, I was elated."

He was also ready to head on up to Indianapolis, and his friends at Eli Lilly, with whom he had shared the news of his illness, told him to come on—and while he was there, they would get him in to see a renowned MS expert who happened to practice in the city. Not that Steve doubted the Atlanta diagnosis, but if this guy was such an expert—why not? So, MRI results in hand, he went to see the neurologist in Indianapolis, where he received a very different diagnosis. "What this doctor told me," recalls Steve, "was that my MS was 'advanced and pervasive'—that it was in my brain and in my spinal cord, and that, frankly, I was going to have a lot of trouble with it." When Steve reported what the neurologist in Atlanta had said, the Indianapolis specialist made him promise that the first thing did when he got back to Atlanta was find another neurologist.

Back home, says Steve, it was his mother-in-law who told him that Shepherd Center had recently hired a new MS specialist, a neurologist named Ben Thrower. "That sounded good to me," says Steve. "I would have gone there in the first place if I had known they had a neurologist on staff." What Dr. Thrower had to say was "word for word" what the doctor in Indianapolis had said. Both doctors also cautioned that the disease would affect Steve's memory and that to continue to practice law might not be wise. "I told Dr. Thrower I wasn't ready to quit quite yet," says Steve, "and he told me, 'Just be careful.'"

As it turned out, Steve practiced law for another three years—more diligently than he ever had before. "It was hard," he says. "But I had the best clients in the world—Eli Lilly, Bayer, Wyeth—people who had put a lot of trust in me and whom I couldn't let down." So Steve was in his office until eleven or twelve o'clock at night, night after night, checking and rechecking his work, making sure he hadn't made any mistakes, making sure he hadn't forgotten anything.

Dr. Thrower, meanwhile, was doing everything in his power to slow the progress of Steve's disease. This also proved difficult. Steve did not respond well to the so-called "ABC" MS drugs: Avonex, Betaseron, and Copaxone. Dr. Thrower tried Rituxan, a drug used to battle non-Hodgkin's lymphoma; he tried Novantrone, a leukemia medication. These drugs produced little benefit but all the unpleasant side-effects experienced by people going through chemotherapy, so Dr. Thrower decided they would stick with Solu-Medrol and wait for the promising new drug, Tysabri to become available.

"We didn't have to wait too terribly long," says Steve. "Tysabri came out—an infusion you take once a month—and it was like night and day. It was the best thing I had taken, by far." Then, no sooner had Steve taken his second treatment than he got word the FDA had taken Tysabri off the market. "I was absolutely devastated," he says. But Steve was not the only MS patient out there for whom this drug had worked like nothing else, and Dr. Thrower was part of a group trying to get it back on the market. He told Steve that the FDA had formed an advisory committee to hold hearings on the drug, that 40 people from around the country would be allowed to testify, and that Steve needed to be one of the 40. In fact, Steve was invited to testify, and he made the trip to Silver Springs, Maryland, in the company of Bill Fowler, a friend of Steve's and also a great friend (and board member) of Shepherd Center.

From his work representing the pharmaceutical industry, Steve happened to know a couple of the FDA committee members, and during one of the breaks in testimony he took it upon himself to buttonhole the guy. "I told him, 'Listen, I know where you live, and I will come after you, so you really need to vote "yes" to bring this drug back to market.'" He did, and the FDA did, and when Tysabri returned to the market, Steve was one of the first to resume its use. "Two years ago, I needed a walker," he says. "Now I'm moving along fine with just a cane." It can't reverse the disease, he explains; it can't recreate nerve cells that are already gone, but it does slow the progression and alleviate some of the symptoms.

Nor can it restore Steve's memory, which he finds perhaps the most frustrating effect of the disease. "It's very odd because sometimes I can remember things clearly and sometimes I can't—which means that I can't depend on my memory." So his life is organized by his desk calendar and by sticky-notes on the refrigerator—to remind him, for example, of the meetings of the Shepherd Center Foundation Board of Trustees, to which he was recently appointed ("a tremendous honor," he says), or, increasingly, the meetings of the fundraising committee for Shepherd's 2009 Legendary Party, of which he is co-chair. It helps, he says gratefully, that Nelson Mullins Riley & Scarborough, the law firm from which he retired, has allowed him to keep his office there, with e-mail and secretarial help.

There's one activity, though, for which his appointment book is unnecessary: the inordinate amount of time he spends as a volunteer at Shepherd Center. The setting of the sun is enough to remind him to head over to Shepherd's ABI unit—because that's where he goes virtually every night. That volunteer role began through his work as a "Stephen minister" at Northside Methodist Church. "This was back eight or nine years ago," says Steve. "We got a call from a church in Alabama—another church with a Stephen ministry—telling us about a young man from their congregation who was coming to Shepherd with a brain injury. Would one of us go visit him? Well, everybody looked at me, and I said I'd be happy to go over there. I've been going ever since."

Steve talks to the patients and their families, he helps out, and he bears witness to the "unbelievable work" that goes on in the ABI unit. "I tell family members that it's like their son or daughter is a youngster again—relearning everything, how to walk, talk, feed themselves, how to use the bathroom. I tell them that it takes time, but it all will come back. Most important, I tell them that they're in the right place, that no other place does it better than Shepherd."

Steve has many stories about patients he's "had the privilege of becoming friends with" at Shepherd. A favorite is that of Zach Phillips, a paralegal from a law firm in Washington, who was hit by a car and landed on its windshield. He was rushed to George Washington's intensive care unit. At the time, his mother, Karen, was in Paris, and

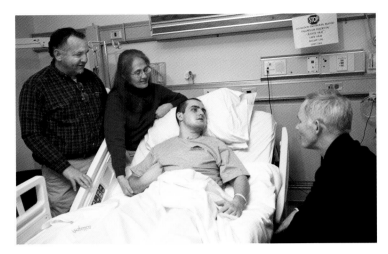

Steve welcomes newly admitted patient, Matthew White, and his parents Mark and Elizabeth from Pikeville, KY.

when she received word of the accident, she began a 24-hour-long journey back to the States. When she finally arrived at the hospital, she found her son in a coma. The doctors were unable to give her a prognosis of any kind, except to say that it was a "touch and go" situation.

Karen had heard of Shepherd through friends who had had a great experience there, and she felt that that was where Zach would have the best chance. Alerted to Zach's situation, Shepherd sent a team to Washington to evaluate whether he would be a good candidate for admission. Their decision was to admit Zach and watch him for three weeks to see if he were making progress. Meanwhile, Steve got a call from a lawyer-friend in Zach's office, telling him about Zach's arrival in Atlanta and asking if Steve would be willing to visit Zach at Shepherd. "He told me not to expect much," says Steve. "He said Zach probably wouldn't even know I was there, but that it would make him feel better to know that somebody had looked in on him."

Zach was indeed still in a coma when Steve first visited, but it was Karen who needed to hear what Steve had to say. "I told her, 'Mrs. Phillips, don't be discouraged. You are in the right place, and Zach is going to do well here. In fact, I can promise you that your son will be able to do everything he could do before the accident, or very close to it, when he leaves here."

It was clear to Steve that Karen wanted to believe him, but he wasn't a doctor, and the doctors in Washington had given no indication that any return to normalcy was possible. "I admitted to her that I wasn't a doctor, but that I seen the miraculous events that occurred at Shepherd on the ABI ward." Exactly one year after his accident, Zach returned to work as a paralegal. Right now, reports Steve, he's in the process of changing careers and is exploring a number of new fields. He occasionally drives down to Atlanta from his home in Tennessee and always calls Steve for lunch or dinner when he's in town. "It's just amazing to see him, to see how he's doing, and it's all because of Shepherd. Only because of Shepherd."

On Sundays, though, you won't find Steve in the ABI unit. You'll find him in the auditorium at Shepherd Center, in his role as "the" usher for the Sunday service. "We don't need a lot of ushers," he laughs. This is another routine he doesn't need sticky-notes for. At noon, when the regular Sunday service is over at Northside Methodist, he heads straight to Shepherd. "I get there in time for lunch," he says. "It's fried chicken on Sunday, so it's better than whatever we would have at home. Then I go up to the auditorium—give out the bulletin and do whatever I can to help

Steve visits with Zach Phillips following his recovery.

people get comfortable." Steve explains that Shepherd makes sure that everybody who wants to attend can attend—beds can be rolled in, ventilators can be plugged in—and that the service usually draws between 50 and 75 people. He stays on afterward for another hour or so, he says, so he can "really talk to all those folks and get to know them."

Well, okay, there are aspects of Steve's life that don't involve Shepherd. There's his family—wife Kay and two sons, one a freshman at South Carolina and the other at Atlanta's Woodward Academy. There are the vacations to Sea Island, where his in-laws have a place, and where Steve enjoys a little refreshment by the pool every bit as much as the next guy. There are the many other organizations he's affiliated with, and the countless friends with whom he's always happy to socialize. As he puts it with characteristic self-deprecation, "I do lunches awfully well."

But make no mistake: it's not a normal life. After all, there is the MS—with the endless rounds of medication, with Dr. Thrower's rules ("Don't ever drive at night unless you know exactly where you're going!"), with the thousand nagging constraints that the disease imposes.

That's not the main thing, though. What makes Steve's life unusual is that, instead of hoarding what the MS hasn't robbed him of, he gives it away so freely. What's unusual is a life so infused with generosity, kindness, and the quiet joy that comes from service to others. What's wonderful is that instead of being diminished by disease, Steve Lore's life is so full that it spills over.

From Buckeye to Flowering Peach

*I*N 1996, ATLANTA GOT LUCKY WHEN A BUCKEYE DECIDED TO TRANSFORM HERSELF INTO A PEACH. Seven years later, when she was diagnosed with MS, Treva Turner will tell you she got lucky—to have discovered Shepherd Center. But first things first . . .

Growing up with three older brothers and nothing ever on the family TV except for sports, Treva was pretty much destined to major in sports journalism during her years at Ohio State. Atlanta's break came when she was lured south by an internship in Emory University's sports information department. Treva has been here ever since. "The Olympics were coming," she says. "There was work available. I was excited to be here." For the record, Treva does not insist on referring to her alma mater as "the Ohio State University," but she admits that "dealing with the whole SEC environment has been an adjustment."

These days, she satisfies the sports craving by working during basketball season as the Atlanta Hawks' media assistant, supplying the broadcast and print folks the information they need to write their stories. "I make sure they have all the records, stats, and player bios—for the opposing team members, too," Treva explains. "Then, at the end of the game, I keep the NBA league office updated with game results. It's fun, especially with the Hawks winning."

Meanwhile, Treva's full-time job is with Time Warner, in a relatively new division called TW Telecom, which provides Internet and data services for the parent company in Atlanta. "It's not too far from journalism," she says, "since I do presentations and write stuff for the VP and the GM. It's still communications, even if it's not sports related." She's happy to report that the company is doing well, in spite the state of the economy.

Back in the fall of 2003, though, the Ohio

native must have wondered if the transformation would prove successful after all. That's when Treva noticed her first symptoms: she couldn't taste anything because of numbness in her mouth, and there was numbness, too, on the left side of her face. Strange stuff—but Treva had recently had a root canal and figured that had to be the cause. She returned to her dentist, but his X-rays failed to detect any problem. Her regular doctor couldn't find anything wrong either and advised her to give the symptoms a chance to go away on their own. That didn't happen. Instead, says Treva, "I noticed that my eyesight was getting very blurry, and that scared me, obviously."

A physician at Emory suspected MS and referred Treva to a neurologist, whose tests, including an MRI, confirmed the unwelcome diagnosis. The news was disturbing enough. How Treva got the news didn't help.

"It was kind of a scary situation," says Treva. "It was the day before Thanksgiving, and I was about to make a ten-hour drive back home to Ohio, and this neurologist calls me and tells me over the phone that I have MS. She said that when I got back she would give me some tapes to look at to decide what course of therapy I wanted." Knowing little about MS, and not seeing too many other options, Treva followed the doctor's orders. "I got back from the holiday and went to her office, and she gave me a bunch of tapes with therapies and said, 'Here they are. You pick one.'"

Treva doesn't mind admitting to being proactive when it comes to her own health, and she quickly turned to the Internet to begin reading up on MS. The more she found out, the less comfortable she was with the idea of choosing her own course of treatment. She called her primary care physician and asked for another recommendation. "He told me to try Dr. Thrower at Shepherd Center," says Treva. "He said he had heard good things about him and about Shepherd."

Again Treva followed "doctor's orders," but this time, she says, "it was like coming home. I can't explain it any other way because Dr. Thrower was so attentive to me and to the questions I had—which were several." There was so much she didn't know about MS, Treva explains, and so many issues to consider—like her age, her desire to have children, what a future with MS looked like. She needed help, and she found it. "Dr. Thrower took all the time I needed, put my X-rays up and went over everything he was looking at; explained it all to me." He also agreed, when Treva told him her story, that a telephone call is probably not the best way to tell someone she has a chronic, progressive, degenerative disease.

But Treva hastens to add that what some other neurologist did or did not do is not the point. The point is "the comfort level I felt with Dr. Thrower, especially since I didn't have the support system of family here in Atlanta. They're 600 miles away." Treva says her mother keeps telling her she needs to move back closer to home. "I tell her I'm not going anywhere. I'm not leaving Shepherd Center unless Dr. Thrower leaves."

What Treva especially appreciates is Dr. Thrower's proactive approach—that he's so determined to stay on top of her disease and to find the therapy that works the best and hurts the least. She was on Copaxone at first—a daily injection, self-administered. It seemed to be working well, says Treva, until she had an MRI that Dr. Thrower didn't like the look of. "He sat me down and said, 'Tell me the truth. I know the injections are kind of hard, having to do them every day, so how are you doing with that?' I said, 'To be honest with you, my life is pretty full, and it's kind of hard to remember it every day.'"

They switched to Rebif, another self-administered injection, but three times a week instead

Treva with Dr. Ben Thrower.

of every day. Treva didn't like it. The flu-like symptoms were an expected side effect; she could deal with those. But the shots just hurt. Then, based on a follow-up MRI, Dr. Thrower "still wasn't happy with what he was seeing," so they tried again. "We've just got to find the right match for you and your body," Dr. Thrower told her.

Meanwhile, says Treva, her education under Dr. Thrower was continuing: "Listen, I'm a very analytical person, always asking a thousand questions. He explains the white spots and the dark spots and how he can tell which are newer and which are older. And what that means—that the ones that have been there for a while are the ones that indicate permanent damage, cells that can't be regenerated." At the same time, Treva was still doing research on her own, "getting a ton of inaccurate information, and he talks me through all that too."

After Rebif, Dr. Thrower prescribed Betaseron. Treva says it's been working "very, very well." She gives herself the injection every other day, in the evening; that way, if she notices any flu symptoms, she can take an Advil, "and I'm fine the next day." That's the critical issue, feeling "good to go" in the morning. "MS or no," she explains, "I still have to work; still have to pay bills and health insurance. So it's crucial to stay productive in my job and stay well enough to keep that job."

Treva feels fortunate to have found the right medication and fortunate to have found Dr. Thrower, with whom she feels she has the best chance to 'manage' the disease. Still, MS remains strange, unpredictable, and, to this point, incurable, and even with the Betaseron, Treva still has to deal with the occasional "flare-up." Oddly, the symptoms might be different every time. The numbness in her mouth has not returned, nor the blurry vision. "But I've experienced some pretty bad vertigo, and most recently, about six months ago, it was mostly a balance issue. I never fell down, but I felt like I just couldn't keep my balance."

How long does such an episode last? Maybe a week, unless you're Treva Turner. "They say if it lasts a week or more, it probably is a flare-up and you need to call the doctor. But I don't wait that long. I don't want to risk any more damage than necessary. After three days, I know I'm not making it up, so I call Dr. Thrower, and he's always very good about getting me in immediately to take care of it."

The fire can generally be extinguished by a three-day IV of Solu-Medrol—the steroid. Treva lives near the hospital, so there's little inconvenience, but the flare-ups do bring the work issue back to the forefront. More reason for Treva to be thankful for her relationship with Dr. Thrower. "I can be totally straightforward with him," she says. "I can tell him that I don't want anybody at work to think that MS is keeping me away. And he'll work with me. He and the staff will figure out a way around my work schedule."

Indeed, for Treva—and probably for many others who have both MS and a job they don't want to lose—a delicate balance must be struck. Treva has not told her colleagues at work that she has MS, but neither has she made any particular effort to keep it a secret. "If the people I work with were interested enough, they could find out exactly what I have," she says. "But I don't make a point of telling people because I don't want them to see the MS before they see me." And she certainly doesn't want her superiors to think that, because of MS, she couldn't handle a promotion or additional responsibilities.

So Treva doesn't talk about her MS at work. Treva certainly doesn't complain about her MS at work. "Nobody is ever going to hear me say [that] I can't do this or that because I have MS. I never want to use MS as a crutch. I don't see it as a crutch. I have good days and bad days, just like anybody else." Treva credits her mom for coming up with the truest words about her condition: "Whenever I'm talking to her on the phone and having one of my little pity moments, she reminds me that I have MS; MS doesn't have me."

There's yet another reason not to talk about her MS, says Treva. "You can't help but feel a certain stigma about it, a sense that you're somehow defective. And it's so hard to explain. Most people don't know anything about it or understand anything about it." That's why it took her a couple of years to work up the courage to tell her own family—and why some extended family members still don't know. At the same time, that's what makes Treva so appreciative of the support system she's had at Shepherd. "It's been so incredible and so important. Not just Dr. Thrower, but all the people on the staff, his nurse Tracy Walker, everybody."

That includes, too, the MS support groups that Dr. Thrower has introduced Treva to. Talking to other people who are going through the same thing, says Treva, "reminds you that you're not alone, and that it's not a death sentence." She adds that it's especially nice to talk to people who know just what it feels like to have to take those shots. "You get a lot of compassion from other people that have MS," she says, "which I've found very comforting." And there's something else she has in common with the others in her support groups: "Every one of them loves Shepherd Center."

When you call, somebody's there, when you need something, you get a call back. That's how I ended up at Shepherd, at this place where I feel so much compassion. You can't put a price on what that means when you're going through something like MS.

What it all comes down to for Treva is care—not just caring for the patient, but caring about the patient. "When you call, somebody's there," she says. "When you need something, you get a call back." Treva was particularly touched to get a call one evening about eight o'clock. "It was from a guy I hadn't even met before, but he was calling well after normal work hours just to let me know that I was being taken care of, that my Solu-Medrol treatment was scheduled to begin two days later. It's just so reassuring to know that somebody cares, that somebody takes an interest." Treva is glad she asked all those questions and "got proactive" early on. "That's how I ended up at Shepherd, at this place where I feel so much compassion. You can't put a price on what that means when you're going through something like MS."

All that remains is convincing those three older brothers, way off in Ohio, that she's where she needs to be, and Treva's working on that. "They don't know anything about Shepherd," she says. "They don't know Dr. Thrower. So I told them, 'Hey, Christopher Reeve was a big supporter of this place.' I knew I was name-dropping, but I really wanted to convey how great Shepherd was. I wanted them to feel as good about my being here as I do."

So how did that work? "All of a sudden they were like, 'Well, if Christopher Reeve supports Shepherd, they must have something pretty big going on.' They're starting to think their little sister's in the right place after all."

Peer Support

For the solace she has received from her peer support group, Treva Turner can thank Diane Baggett, who acts as the facilitator of MS peer support at Shepherd as well as the link between the National MS Society and the Shepherd group.

Diane has been an MS patient at Shepherd since 2001, but her history with the hospital goes back even farther. As she explains, "Back in 1993 I was having symptoms of fatigue and clumsiness and found out that Shepherd had a post-polio clinic. I had had polio in 1953, so I went to Dr. Don Leslie, who at the time was head of the post-polio clinic, and he confirmed the post-polio diagnosis." Eight years later, says Diane, she developed some new symptoms, different from post-polio, and her primary care physician suggested that she get Dr. Leslie to recommend a neurologist. "Dr. Ben Thrower had just come to Shepherd, so I went to him and he gave me the MRI that certified me as a "classic" MS patient."

Diane recalls that back in 1993 she had been helped by joining a post-polio support group, and, then, right after she received her MS diagnosis, she had an unexpected encounter that reminded her how important a little encouragement can be. "I was by myself," she says, "just leaving Dr. Thrower's office, and I ran right into Dr. Leslie coming around the corner. When I told him about the diagnosis, he told me, 'You'll be OK. You're like the Energizer Bunny. You'll just keep right on going.' I've always remembered how lucky I was to run into him like that."

There wasn't an MS peer support group at the time, but Diane figured there needed to be. So at her suggestion, Dr. Dean Erickson, Ph.D., who was the MS Center's neuropsychologist at the time, "began to get together with four or five us to get a support group started." Subsequently, group members (including Diane) underwent the official training, via the Georgia Chapter of the National MS Society, to get designated as a qualified support group, and the result is SHEPS (Self Help and Education Among Peers), Shepherd's monthly support group for MS patients.

Diane describes herself as the "link" between her group and the Georgia Chapter of the National MS Society. "When they send out announcements about activities they're having, or any other pertinent information, I forward it along to our members." The monthly meetings take place at Shepherd, where "five or so" group members are usually in attendance. Sometimes the meetings are informational—as when a physical therapist from ProMotion demonstrates a potentially beneficial exercise technique, for example—but, says Diane, "mostly it's just peers sharing with each other."

How do those peers find out about the group? According to Dr. Robert Godsall, Ph.D., the MS neuropsychologist who four years ago took Dr. Erickson's place as the staff representative for SHEPS, most of them find out on their own. "My experience is that most of our MS patients are very proactive. It's amazing how they seek out information by themselves. They go on the Internet, they Google, and get all kinds of information. Then, if they want something more, or feel like there's something missing with regard to how they're living with

Pete Anziano, Manager, Peer Mentoring Program.

their MS, they might go to the Shepherd Center website and call our number." When that happens, says Dr. Godsall, "I refer those folks over to Diane Baggett, who is the nominal chairperson of the group."

Of course, Shepherd had peer support long before Shepherd had an MS Center. The program's roots go back to the early 1980s, when Curtis Rodgers, toward the end of his six months of therapy following a construction accident, began talking to new spinal cord injured patients as they arrived at Shepherd. Curtis was among the dozen or so former patients who officially instituted "peer support" in 1984, and he subsequently became program manager.

Today, the face of the peer support program for spinal cord injury is Pete Anziano, an Atlanta native who found himself at Shepherd after a motorcycle accident in 2004 sent him first to Johnson City Medical Center in Tennessee for acute trauma care. "I knew of Shepherd, having grown up here," says Pete, "but it helped that my then-mother-in-law, Judy Spaulding, was

Minna Hong, Peer Support Coordinator.

then and is still working at Shepherd. She played an integral role in my admission here, and I'm eternally grateful to her for the good things that have happened to me at Shepherd."

Some of those good things, says Pete, happened during his year in the Marcus Community Bridge Program, for which he signed up after his inpatient rehab. "That program is so great. They got me in touch with vocational rehabilitation; they helped me get my house modified so I could more easily shower and dress in the mornings; they got my car outfitted with hand controls so I could drive again."

Some other good things happened because Pete made them happen. "I wanted to keep up my personal therapy program," he says, "so on my own I would come into the ProMotion gym here at Shepherd and exercise every day. Then, if I had a couple of extra minutes I would head up to the gyms on the second and third floors, the inpatient therapy gyms. I maintained a presence there just in case the therapists wanted me to demonstrate an advanced wheelchair skill or something like that." He continued to help out "on a hit-and-miss basis," he says, "but then people started coming back to me saying, 'You know, when you showed me how to do this or that, that's when I realized it was going to be OK. I knew that I too could do it.'" When he started getting that kind of feedback, he realized what he needed to be doing. "It felt so good to know that I had helped somebody else—given them some kind of tool or skill that they would be able to use for the rest of their lives." It wasn't long before Pete learned that there was a name for what he was doing—peer support—and that "there was a peer support program already in place here being run by Minna Hong."

Pete says he took it upon himself to get to know Minna better, "and more important, let her get to know me." What Minna found out was that Pete was "more or less the 'center cut' of the demographic voted most likely to be a spinal cord injured patient—early 30s (at the time), male, and a risk taker"—and that he was ideally suited to help out in the peer support program. At the same time, says Pete, Minna was being given the opportunity to expand her responsibilities at the center, "so I, in turn, was offered the job of handling about 50 percent of the responsibility of managing the peer support program."

Of course, Pete didn't start out as a peer supporter. First he had to be a "supportee," and he admits it wasn't easy. "I'm just bullheaded," he admits, "and my feeling after my injury was that I was going to have to hunker down and take care of it myself. My problem, and my own to deal with." He says he was in the therapy gym one day, trying to figure out how to get from the floor back into his chair, and he just couldn't do it, couldn't master that very necessary skill. "I was ready to give up, to accept that this was something I wasn't going to be able to change, when my therapist called somebody in to demonstrate this skill, somebody who was living in a chair, a peer supporter as I later came to understand."

That peer supporter turned out to be Minna Hong. "She came in," says Pete, "weighing maybe 95 pounds—tiny little lady—and she got down on the floor and popped her butt back up in that chair and made it look like it was no big deal at all." At that point Pete "knew it was real," he says. "Until I saw Minna, I wasn't paying too much attention to what people were telling me I could do . She was living it. That made it real for me and also gave me the idea that I could do it myself. Later on came the realization that I could help others—which I have found to be eternally rewarding."

You can be 10 years post injury, out in the community somewhere, and just reach out to the proper peer support program at Shepherd, and we'll do what we can for you. We're always there, always free, no enrollment necessary, and folks that might need us are always welcome.

—Pete Anziano

Peer support for spinal cord injury "lives under the umbrella of the Marcus Community Bridge Program," says Pete. But he's quick to point out that you don't have to be enrolled in the Bridge Program to join the group. "You can be 10 years post injury, out in the community somewhere, and just reach out to the peer support program at Shepherd, and we'll do what we can for you. We're always there, always free, no enrollment necessary, and folks that might need us are always welcome."

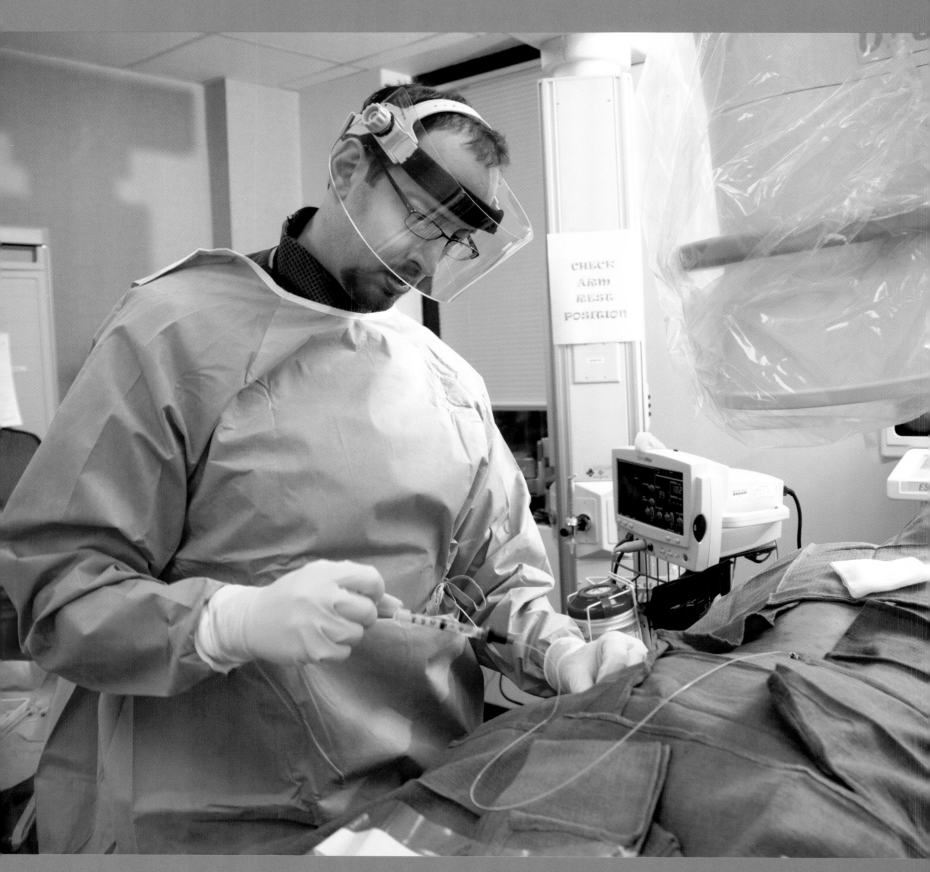

Dr. Erik Shaw performing an epidural procedure on a patient.

THE DEAN STROUD PAIN INSTITUTE

Shepherd Center's Dean Stroud Pain Institute was formally inaugurated in 2008, but by that time Shepherd had already had a designated pain treatment facility for a decade. Recognizing the need to treat and manage the pain of patients who had suffered spinal cord or brain injury, the pain clinic was originally established across the street at 2045 Peachtree Road and staffed on a contract basis. Its rapid evolution into the world-class facility it is today is hardly surprising, because using every imaginable means to restore people to the fullest and most productive life possible is what Shepherd does.

So it is that Dr. Erik Shaw, D.O., takes justifiable pleasure in showing off the gleaming corridors, the 10 treatment rooms, the surgical areas, and the fluoroscopy suites that now comprise the Dean Stroud Pain Institute. The expansive new space became available, explains Dr. Shaw, when the Jane Woodruff Pavilion was completed and the doctors' offices were moved up to the sixth floor. At this point, in early 2010, there's room enough to share with physicians who are not part of the Pain Institute, but that may not be the case for long. "We're making good use of it," says Dr. Shaw. "During clinic time, seven or eight of the 10 treatment rooms are likely to be filled, and we'll see 20 patients during the average four-hour treatment day. It stays hopping."

Dr. Shaw believes the clinic will become even busier as word spreads that it's open not only to those who are already patients in Shepherd's spinal cord injury, brain injury, or MS units, but to anybody looking for chronic pain relief. "There's a big population out there who really could benefit from what we offer," he explains. "And what we offer, to a greater extent than the rest of the pain community in Atlanta, is a diversified range of treatments, for a very wide range of pain syndromes. We don't do just injections; it's our job to treat the whole person, and that may well involve not only treating pain, but psychological counseling and physical therapy as well. It's incredibly important to offer these resources, to try to help our patients as completely as possible."

Dr. Erik Shaw

Erik Shaw was born and raised in Houston, Texas, where he was a student at St. John's prep school and then, he says, "chose to go to Texas A&M because they offered me a scholarship." He majored in biomedical engineering, which served him well when he didn't get into med school the first time around. By the time he was accepted, he'd been offered a job by Lockheed Martin working on the MIR space station program. "I would be one of 40 Americans on the project," he says, "traveling back and forth from Houston to Moscow. It was an opportunity I couldn't pass up."

After a year and a half in the MIR program, during which he served with Shannon Lucid, John Blaha and other astronauts, Dr. Shaw returned to school and received his D.O. degree from the University of North Texas Health Science Center in Fort Worth. His training continued with a residency in Physical Medicine and Rehabilitation and an Anesthesiology fellowship in Pain Medicine at the University of Texas Health Science Center in San Antonio.

Between his undergraduate degree in biomedical engineering ("which looks at the electrical and mechanical systems of the human body") and his D.O., Dr. Shaw is uniquely qualified for the work he finds himself in. "The study of osteopathy has given me a better knowledge of musculo-skeletal medicine, along with a fundamental philosophy that addresses the balance of the whole

Dr. John T. Musser

human body. My biomedical engineering helped me understand the body's complex systems, and my osteopathic training really complemented that knowledge. I have the advantage of a sort of three-dimensional perspective, which helps me do all I can for these patients."

Dr. Shaw's arrival at Shepherd was a matter of fortunate coincidence. When Shepherd first decided to bring the pain clinic in-house, it hired Dr. Bert Blackwell, who happened to be Dr. Shaw's colleague and good friend, though a couple of years ahead of him in the fellowship program in San Antonio. "Dr. Blackwell came in took the place of, like, three physicians," says Dr. Shaw, "so he was quickly overwhelmed. He really wanted Shepherd to hire a second doctor, but at the same time he asked the hospital to hold off until I had finished my training and then to give me a look. They did both, and then they hired me in 2006." The two friends worked together for two and a half years; then, at the end of 2008, Dr. Blackwell took a job in Greenville, South Carolina, to be closer to his hometown.

A half-year after Dr. Blackwell's departure, and much to Dr. Shaw's relief, Shepherd hired Dr. John T. Musser, newly graduated from Emory, to join the Pain Institute as its first Fellow. In addition to helping with the case load, Dr. Musser brings great knowledge about nutrition, says Dr. Shaw, "from a truly scientific point of view, which has really helped broaden our perspective. Sometimes an inexpensive supplement, like Vitamin D, can help balance a patient's internal physiology, maybe by counteracting medicines they've been taking for a long time. It's one more avenue by which we can help our patients."

Also part of the team is clinical psychologist Dr. Urszula Klich, Ph.D., whose specialties include not only psychological evaluation, but also muscle relaxation through biofeedback, medita-

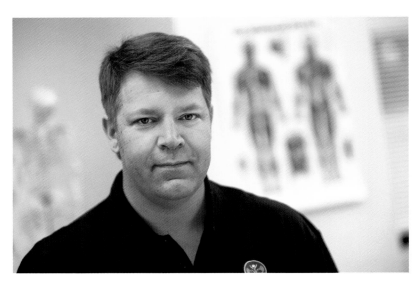
Chris Nesbitt, physical therapist

tion, and group-based pain education. "What she does is incredibly important," says Dr. Shaw, "because so many patients have anxiety and tension that they're not even always aware of. Plus, chronic pain has a way of bringing out people's underlying psychopathologies, and having a trained psychologist on staff is critical. She is always there for our patients."

The Pain Institute team also includes physical therapist Chris Nesbitt, who comes to Shepherd, says Dr. Shaw, "with a theology degree, a behavioral health background, and experience with troubled teens—not to mention his Masters in Physical Therapy from the Medical College of Georgia." The only problem with Chris, jokes Dr. Shaw, is that "he's so dedicated to working one-on-one with each patient, it really limits his volume." Of course, chronic pain sufferers who are afraid to move their bodies need exactly the kind of individualized therapy Nesbitt offers. "He has tremendous expertise," says Dr. Shaw.

Three nurses and three medical assistants round out the team, and for the dedicated service of each of them Dr. Shaw is deeply grateful. "A tremendous amount of work, of detail, has to be handled when you're seeing 20 patients on a given day. The whole team does a great job of working together to keep things moving smoothly."

Articulating the Pain Institute's mission, Dr. Shaw offers a short answer: "to help to treat a wide variety of pain syndromes in a thoughtful, deliberative, and complete manner in order to help restore health and life."

What really sets this clinic apart, though, begins with Dr. Shaw's acknowledgment that "pain management across the country is often misunderstood and much maligned, because there has been a lot of abuse of the system." Pain treatment might begin with an injection, but Dr. Shaw and his staff make certain that it doesn't end there. "Sticking a needle in someone's body safely, even if it's in the cervical spine, can be taught to any physician who knows anatomy and has reasonably dexterous hands. It's a question of knowing when to do what, when to stop, when to switch gears, and how to really to respond to the patient." Sometimes, he says, the most important part is listening to patients, "understanding what they're telling you about their anxiety and stress." Chronic pain disrupts sleep and work, as well as health; it can bring on depression, which, Dr. Shaw points out, can lead to a whole host of other problems. "There's a lot going on beyond the specific symptom the patient articulates, and the good pain specialist is going to try to treat the whole person, not stop with the injection."

Of course, the right medicine and the right medical procedures are important, and the technology and expertise available at Shepherd's Pain Institute are unsurpassed. Dr. Shaw notes that the opportunity to work with Shepherd's catastrophically injured patients has given him and his staff an invaluable range of experience—"the kind of experience you can't find in a whole lot of places." Sometimes pain treatment calls for "pretty sophisticated implanted devices," particularly when pain is radiating from a specific point of origin, like the central nervous system. "We use spinal cord stimulators, and specialized medicine injected via intrathecal pumps—which penetrate to the same layer as a spinal tap, but instead of taking fluid out, you're putting medicine in through a small catheter. New medicines are coming on the market all the time which offer great potential for this kind of procedure."

Dr. Urszula Klich

Still, Dr. Shaw emphasizes that the most high-tech, most expensive, and newest technologies don't add up to the right prescription for all, or even most, patients. Advocating a multidisciplinary approach, the Pain Institute addresses the whole person with a full range of therapies—at the same time that it seeks to make those healing therapies known to a wider population of pain sufferers.

"I do think there are a great many people out there, boomer-age," he says, "who are experiencing a host of pain issues—knee pain, back pain, shoulder pain—and who assume that these are things they have to live with. I'm talking about active people, who want to stay active, but who assume that their activity is going to hurt more and more and that they have to live with the pain." They don't, insists Dr. Shaw. "In many cases, there are some pretty simple things we can do that can really help." So a big goal in the coming years is to spread the word—through primary care doctors, though word of mouth—"and to begin to realize the great potential we have to help that particular population."

Dr. Shaw believes he is in a good place to pursue that ambition. He and his wife Lali are happy to call Atlanta home, and he relishes the short five-mile commute to work. Most important, he's been warmly embraced by the Shepherd community.

"From Alana Shepherd on down," he says, "through the rest of the family, the hospital's benefactors, its volunteers, and of course its staff, we're one community here, all focused on bringing the best possible care to these patients. Whether they've had dramatic trauma, or MS, or chronic pain, there's just this fundamental desire to help our patients, to get people the care they need." Dr. Shaw mentions patients that have come to him with previously undiagnosed brain injury. "I'll go to Dr. Bilsky and say, 'Hey, can you help me here?' And of course he wants to, and he can, and he does. That's the community we're all part of here."

But the folks at Shepherd, by and large, are not content to rest on their laurels, and Dr. Shaw is no exception. "Compared to what other people in the city or region are doing in terms of pain management, I'd have to say our system is pretty good. And the health care we offer, from a medical perspective, is at the top. Still, I always feel like, if we could do a little more or work a little harder, we could help a few more people, and that's what we continue to strive for."

Free at Last!

❧

THEY ARE A COUPLE OF SMALL TOWNS SOUTH OF ATLANTA, just a few miles apart. But for Becky Bius, getting from Stockbridge, where she graduated from high school a decade ago, to McDonough, where she now lives and works as a paralegal, has been a long, arduous journey.

The story began, says Becky, when growth spurts during high school stretched her ligaments to the point that it was difficult to move around without falling down. By her senior year, 1999, her mother was taking her to one doctor after another, none of whom successfully diagnosed her problem. "I had tests for lupus," she recalls, "for rheumatoid arthritis; I had doctors wanting to do hip replacements, you name it. They all would try to treat my symptoms, not figure out the problem. They also wanted to medicate me. I was not comfortable taking pain medication. I wanted the problem fixed."

Meanwhile, Becky continued to be unstable—and also in a whole lot of pain. In December 2000, with a referral from another orthopedist, she went to see a sacroiliac specialist at Crawford Long. "He tried a lot of things," says Becky, "physical therapy, injections, to try to tighten up my ligaments so my SI joints would be stabilized. But they had been out for so long that if they were put back in place during therapy, they would be back out five minutes later."

In 2001, Becky's doctor tried a bilateral SI fixation, intended to stabilize Becky's SI joints with pins and screws. "I did better after that," she says. "I wasn't pain free, but at least I could walk without worrying about falling down stairs." Since she was still experiencing some pain, though, Becky continued seeing her physician for physical therapy and follow-up testing. In December of that year, the doctor performed a bilateral fusion of the joints. "That really seemed to help,"

recalls Becky. "I was feeling pretty good, more or less able to go back to my active life—snow skiing and wake-boarding, the kinds of things I had always enjoyed. I was going to the gym a lot. I still had pain, but at this point I decided that I would just live with it."

Then, on a follow-up visit, a CAT scan revealed that the fusion had failed; her body had rejected the grafted bone. "Now it's 2004," says Becky. "My doctor redid the fusion with an artificial joint substance, and I had to wear a bone-growth stimulator. Once I recovered from that, I was still in some pain, but everything had healed and the surgery was deemed successful. And I did pretty well for a couple of years."

But Becky's pain returned, with a vengeance, in 2008. "It seemed to be getting worse day by day," she says. "I couldn't sleep, couldn't do anything. Then it started traveling, and I would get shooting pains down my leg. It was debilitating—it hurt so bad it would take my breath. The worst thing was I was in the middle of trying to plan my wedding."

It [the pain] seemed to be getting worse day by day. I couldn't sleep, couldn't do anything...I would get shooting pains down my leg. It was debilitating—it hurt so bad it would take my breath. The worst thing was, I was in the middle of trying to plan my wedding.

—Becky Bius

Becky resumed physical therapy. She tried acupuncture, herbal remedies, everything. Finally her physical therapist at Crawford Long suggested she go see Dr. Erik Shaw at Shepherd Center. "Based on his evaluation," says Becky, "Dr. Shaw concluded that my pain was nerve pain—from all the scar tissue, all the damage from my repeated surgeries and injections." That diagnosis made sense to Becky, but relief still proved

elusive. "He tried some trigger-point injections; those didn't help. He tried to go in and cauterize some nerve endings, and that didn't help."

At that point, Dr. Shaw brought in Boston Scientific, the company that makes the Precision spinal cord stimulators, and their rep, Bill Cleary. Becky had misgivings. "When I first went to Dr. Shaw," she says, "I told him I didn't want to be medicated, and I didn't want another surgery." But Dr. Shaw and Bill Cleary seemed to Becky to be a good team, and they gave Becky enough confidence to agree to a one-week trial with the device.

"In the end," says Becky, "I did have another surgery, and it changed my life. I now have the spinal cord stimulator. I got it in August, 2009, and it has made all the difference." As Becky ex-

Becky with her husband Nick

plains it, the device's "lead" sits against her spinal cord, in the epidural space between L-4 and L-5, and its wires run down to her hips, which is where the battery is.

Becky says the stimulator emits an electronic pulse, but instead of causing muscles to tense and relax, as other types of stimulators do, this one intercepts pain signals. "So instead of feeling constant pain in my back and hips and down my legs, now I feel a tingle." If pain recurs, the device can be adjusted, or reprogrammed, accordingly. "It's amazing," she says. "It's crazy."

Amazing, also, to reflect on how her pain had transformed her. "Constant pain really takes a toll," she says. "It changes your whole personality. I'm a really active person. I like to go and do, and when that was taken away, it was just depressing. My pain had changed me, physically and mentally."

Now, after eleven years, and, by her count, about 30 doctors, Becky is back. "I feel absolutely wonderful," she says. Any downside? "Well, after about 25 years, they might have to go back in and replace the battery, but that's about it."

Becky is delighted to return to "going and doing." She says she has a "new lease on life" and is excited that she can now experience all that the world has to offer without pain. Also, for the record, the wedding came off as planned, in June 2008, and Becky and her husband are hoping to adopt a baby.

The length of her ordeal measures the depth of Becky's gratitude, and she is quick to declare that Dr. Shaw is "by far the best doctor I've ever been to." And not only because he was able to relieve her pain. "There are a lot doctors out there who seem more interested in money than in their patients," explains Becky. "But Dr. Shaw not only solved my medical problem; he also took time to answer all my questions, to be there for me emotionally, and to wipe away my tears. Because of Dr. Shaw, I have regained my confidence in the medical profession. I count it as a miracle that he is my doctor."

Dr. Shaw is by far the best doctor I've ever been to. He not only solved my medical problem, but he also took time to answer all my questions, to be for me emotionally, and to wipe away my tears. Because of Dr. Shaw, I have regained my confidence in the medical profession.

—Becky Bius

ERB Industries and the
Dean Stroud Pain Institute

Georgia Tech graduate Bill Erb founded Atlanta-based ERB Industries, a safety equipment and apparel manufacturing company more than a half-century ago, and the company has enjoyed remarkable success and longevity. Perhaps more unusual, though, is that as of 1997 the company has been employee-owned and that those employees have proven to be incredibly generous.

The company's employee giving program—via weekly payroll deduction—originally supported a Chicago charity, explains Bonnie Hardage, Shepherd Center Foundation's director of major gifts, "but about a dozen years ago they made the decision to start giving on a more local level." Longtime friends of the Shepherd family, Bill and his wife Florrie thought the employee giving program could be put to great use in support of Shepherd Center. As a result of that decision, as of March 2010 ERB Industries employees had contributed $421,293 "to almost every program we've needed

funds for through the years," says Hardage.

Beginning in December 2007, though, the chief beneficiary of ERB employees' generosity has been Shepherd's pain treatment center, and in recognition of Bill's and the company's extraordinary generosity, the center was officially named the Dean Stroud Pain Institute at Shepherd. The name honors the memory of the Erbs' grandson, Robert "Dean" Stroud, who died at age 13 in a tragic boating accident.

ERB Industries CEO Sheila Eads, who serves on the Shepherd Center's Advisory Board, notes that the company also supports a program that donates 50 cents to Shepherd Center for every order they receive. "Our company is like family," explains Eads, "and we identify with the family approach of Shepherd Center. It is an honor and a privilege to be associated with one of Atlanta's most admired charitable organizations."

Scott Sikes and Dell Sikes

THE SHEPHERD CENTER FOUNDATION

It comes as no surprise that Shepherd's perpetual challenge—how can we do it better?—applies also to the hospital's fundraising efforts. After all, the hospital was largely built through the generosity of donors large and small. To respond to that challenge, the Shepherd Center Foundation and its Board of Trustees were created in 2005, and in 2007 Scott Sikes was lured from his job as VP for external affairs at Valdosta State University to serve as Vice President and Executive Director of the Shepherd Center Foundation.

"But wait a minute," says Sikes. "You can't talk about what's happened at Shepherd over the past 23-plus years without talking about Mr. Dell B. Sikes. It's been said that 'success has many parents and failure is an orphan.' Well, Dell is certainly of those many parents where Shepherd is concerned."

No doubt about it. When Dell Sikes became the hospital's director of development in 1987, Shepherd Spinal Center, as it was known then, was only 12 years old. The Billi Marcus building didn't exist, and no one had ever heard of the Legendary Party. Sikes arrived just in time to help direct the $12 million fundraising campaign that had just been launched, and among the many successes for which he can claim parenthood was the gift from Bernie Marcus, his campaign chairman, of 62,000 shares of Home Depot stock. He recalls with particular pleasure watching Billi Marcus's face when it was announced at the dedication that the building would be named in her honor.

Other highlights marking the Dell Sikes tenure were the extraordinary $17.6 million gift from The Marcus Foundation, which created the Marcus Community Bridge Program, the phenomenal growth of Shepherd's endowment, and, on the eve of his retirement in 2005, the kick-off of the center's $62.6 million Capital & Endowment Campaign. Not surprisingly, "retirement" has proved to be a misnomer. As Scott Sikes explains, "Dell and his wife Mary Ann remain an integral part of the Shepherd Center family as donors and volunteers, and since his retirement Dell has stayed on as an advisor and consultant to the Development department every day—and as a paid employee one day a week."

Speaking of the Shepherd family, Scott Sikes notes "an unusual twist" on that familiar theme. It seems that he and Dell Sikes might very well be very distant cousins. Scott's grandfather Sikes came from Glennville, Georgia, and Dell was born and raised in Glennville. It's likely that they're both descended from the same Revolutionary War soldier who settled near Glennville after that war. "But the relationship, if any," says Scott, "is so distant that only a genealogist or historian could unravel it."

Henry Munford succeeded Dell as Vice President of Development and Community Relations. Munford was instrumental in the creation of the Shepherd Center Foundation and helped shape the staffing structure still utilized by the Development department and Volunteer Services department. Prior to joining Shepherd's staff, Munford was a volunteer and donor himself and one of the founding members of the Junior Committee. He led the fundraising staff during most of the 25th Anniversary Capital & Endowment Campaign and the construction phase of the Jane Woodruff Pavilion.

Elaborating on the creation of the official entity known as the Shepherd Center Foundation, Scott Sikes explains that "It was time to let the hospital board of directors stay focused on the purpose of running the hospital per se, and to create another group to take over all fundraising efforts." Forming such a group was essential, says Sikes, because "from the get-go fundraising has been a key component of what makes Shepherd Shepherd, and it's my personal opinion that one of the main reasons we are so much better than other very fine hospitals is because of our private gifts."

So the Foundation was created to raise money—"to raise money by telling our story to more and more people and then asking those people to become investors in our mission." Sikes clarifies that the Foundation is not a money management entity. "We don't dole it out," he says. "Every penny we raise goes straight through to the hospital, where James Shepherd and the hospital board, working with the CFO and the CEO, make all decisions on how to apportion the budget, including the Foundation money." Sikes adds that the hospital's profit margin is "probably about 5 percent—we're truly a not-for-profit—so the Foundation's money is essential and greatly appreciated."

On the other hand, Sikes does note that, as the Foundation and its work continue to grow, the current modus operandi might change. "The day might come when we hold onto a portion of our money in order to hire more staff and expand our mission. We want to grow nationally, sort of like St. Jude Children's Research Hospital, so it would be appropriate for us to spend something like 16 cents on the dollar to pay salaries, benefits, and operating expenses of increased staff."

The calendar of fundraising events sponsored by the Foundation is remarkable—extensive, varied, and highly successful. In February comes Valentine's Pecans, wherein the Shepherd Center Auxiliary invites you to buy a tin (or two) of delicious pecans for that special someone. April brings Casino Night, the recent creation of the Shepherd Center Society, which itself is a recently created volunteer group, composed mostly of former Junior Committee members looking for new ways to stay involved.

In May comes Derby Day, which at last count has been running for the roses for 27 straight years. The premier event of Shepherd's Junior Committee, Derby Day—according to Sikes—"consists of an entire day of activities, including games, drinks, silent auction, live auction, music,

Bill Furbish excelling in a game of murderball.

etc., all leading up to watching the Kentucky Derby on big-screen TVs for less than two minutes." Next on the calendar is the Shepherd Center Cup, the annual fall-season golf tournament now in its 26th year. Sikes explains that the Shepherd Cup is really two events: a tee-off cocktail party, with live and silent auctions, followed a few days later by the actual tournament.

Shepherd Center's aptly named Legendary Party arrives in November, but, as Sikes explains, events like the Patrons' Party and the volunteers' luncheon have been leading up to it all year long. What's more, while the black-tie ball is in progress, the Junior Committee is hosting yet another party just across the hall. "But it starts a couple of hours after the Legendary Party and lasts a couple of hours later," Sikes explains.

The calendar comes to an end during the November – December holiday season with the Auxiliary's pièce de résistance, Pecans on Peachtree. "Last year alone," says Sikes, "just part of the money the event raised went to reflooring the Livingston Gym—a $45,000 job. What the

121

Scott Sikes credits Vice President of Facilities Wilma Bunch and Engineering Director Henry Burkard for their leadership in creating and maintaining state-of-the-art facilities, which were generously funded by private donations.

Auxiliary does with that event is just incredible." Sikes adds that the Auxiliary is "really the heart and soul of the hospital. In addition to their big event, they're working year-round on the smaller things, like cheerful decorations and gifts for patients at every holiday imaginable."

Sikes says that many organizations hope to break even with such events, "but we hope to make lots of money." And make lots of money they do—somewhere north of $1 million annually. But in putting on those events and raising those monies, the Foundation's work is just beginning. "Our greatest source of revenue is individual donors contributing major gifts," says Sikes; "second is private foundations making major gifts; third is corporations making major gifts; below that would come these fundraising events; then below that come the many, many contributions that we might define as 'less than major' but which are still deeply appreciated." In a typical year Shepherd Center receives contributions from some 5,000 individual donors, including individuals, private foundations, and corporations. Sikes admits that's a lot of folks, but then adds with a wry grin, "Of course, it could be much larger."

With about 35 members, the Foundation Board of Trustees plays its role alongside the hospital Board of Directors and the Shepherd Center Advisory Board, and the three bodies work together, says Sikes, as a sort of career ladder—"to get people who have shown they want to be involved a way to move up the hierarchy." To illustrate, Sikes explains that four longtime Advisory Board members were recently asked to join the Foundation Board of Trustees. "And in three or four years we might take one or more of those people and move them to the hospital board."

In fact, of the Foundation board's several committees—special events, major gifts, planned giving, etc.—one of the most critical is the nominating committee. "That's because we're constantly looking for new folks to come be a part of our effort, folks who could make a contribution of time, talent, or financial resources." This effort brings into view the second major function of the Foundation—to oversee all of Shepherd's volunteer functions. That arrangement makes sense, Sikes explains, because virtually everybody who serves on any of Shepherd's boards initially came to the hospital as a volunteer, or a donor, or both. "Many, many people have come up through the ranks of the Junior Committee," says Sikes. "In fact, at our recent joint meeting of the hospital board, the Foundation Board of Trustees, and the Advisory Board, we had in the room 20 people who were former Junior Committee co-chairs."

Still, Job One is fundraising, and in a hospital renowned for excellence across the board, Sikes and his staff clearly hold up their end of the bargain. "We spend about $100,000 a month to raise about $1 million a month. That's what our whole team of staffers and volunteers accomplishes, and that's a pretty amazing return on investment for the hospital. According to Sikes, Bernie Marcus likes to say that, rather than a great leader or great businessman, he sees himself as simply a great investor—and that Shepherd Center has proven to be his best-ever return on investment.

"That's how I look at our fundraising," says Sikes. "We take time and money out to invest in fundraising work, and we reap a remarkable reward." He cites two keys to this success: "First, Alana Shepherd is and always has been this hospital's real fundraising leader. Because of her, Atlanta's donor community has embraced this great work. And second, if Dell, Henry Munford, or I have done anything particularly well, it's been to bring in smart people—both employees and volunteers—and get out of their way."

Sikes takes justifiable pleasure in imagining the myriad ways the Foundation's money is put to the service of this great hospital. "The hospital is moving toward 'translational research,'" he says, "where we take what's been done in the labs and connect it to the work in the clinics. So we like to think that in a few years we'll be spending a lot of our time fundraising for cure research, for translational research, and being a part of that great effort." Expanding on that idea, Sikes says he likes to compare Shepherd's work to that of a lighthouse, whose beam continually moves from one point of focus to another. "Right now we have been focused on having the most fabulous environment for patients and families of patients—the best possible living arrangements, the best possible medical equipment. Once that piece is complete, we will shine our light all the more brightly on research."

Wherever that light shines, whatever the great work to be undertaken, Sikes and his Foundation staff know that Shepherd Center will be able to continue to depend on a volunteer and donor community unmatched in generosity and commitment. "So much of what we do here at Shepherd has been made possible by our donors," he says, "and that's one reason we are a much better destination for patients than other facilities that are not so fortunate."

"MIDGE TRACY
NEEDS YOU!"

Not every Shepherd volunteer puts in the kind of hours Steve Lore does, but more and more people are volunteering all the time, and they're finding more and more ways to do it. For that, we can thank Midge Tracy.

Midge came to Shepherd as director of Volunteer Services in 1998, shortly after she and her husband moved to Atlanta from Miami. She had served as director of volunteers and development at the Catholic Home for Children in Miami ("before Hurricane Andrew pretty much wiped out the children's shelters"), and she was delighted to return to work she loves at Shepherd. "I've always been a volunteer," she says, "a caregiver by nature. And I've always wanted to work in a hospital as a volunteer. Or, best of all, to get paid for what I really love to do."

Midge directs the efforts of a volunteer corps that has now swelled to some 700 members—a number that has doubled over the past decade. The corps is still anchored by the hospital's renowned Auxiliary, which, since its inception in 1981, has donated countless thousands of hours (and approximately $7 million) to Shepherd Center. Almost as venerable, the Junior Committee has been organizing its signature fund-raiser, Derby Day, since 1983. For the energy and devotion of these veteran organizations, Midge gives all the credit to Alana Shepherd. "Alana really had the vision for what it would mean to be a volunteer at Shepherd," says Midge. "Many of the original volunteers were her close friends, with whom she shared her own passion for the hospital. And many of them, after 33 years, are still here, and their children are here, and even their grandchildren are here. The role model is Alana."

In 2000, under Midge's stewardship, the new Peach Corps was established. This offshoot of the Auxiliary gives younger members the opportunity to get their children involved in the volunteer effort. "It's a wonderful program," says Midge. "The parents bring their children, and the children bring their brightness." Twice a year the Peach Corps puts on a cookout or an ice cream social for the patients and families. During holidays the children give out goody baskets or write "courage cards" to the patients. The parents bring the kids by the security desk "so the folks there can make sure they don't have a cold or anything; then they get a little sticker that says, 'I'm OK to visit.'"

"You can be three years old and learn that it's a fun thing to give to other people," says Midge, and, just as important, the program shows the youngsters that people with disabilities are not scary. "It's amazing how quickly they become accustomed to seeing people in wheelchairs." Of course, the program is really about bringing an unexpected burst of joy to the patient's day. "Imagine you're having a tough day," says Midge, "and this little kid shows up at your room and says, 'I have a present for you.'" That's the mission of the Peach Corps: "any activity that makes a patient's or family's day brighter."

Midge has also spearheaded the effort to increase the numbers of what she calls "independent volunteers." These are the folks who are not really interested in joining a group, Midge

Midge Tracy, Director of Volunteer Services.

explains, but who just want to help on their own, on their own schedule, an hour or two a week. Their help is important because it's on-site, and they can be called upon, often at the last minute, to come in and help with a particular task. The Breakfast Club is a great example, says Midge—where volunteers, sometimes retirees, sometimes people on the way to work, will come in at 6:45 A.M. and help take the breakfast trays to the patients and even help with the feeding when necessary. "It's a huge help, as you can imagine."

Plenty of other opportunities are available, too. Volunteers can help support the therapy staff during locomotor training or aquatic exercise, or assist in wheelchair cleaning and maintenance, or deliver patients' mail and gifts, or run the cash register at the coffee shop, or even serve as the greeter at the Welcome Desk—just to name a few. "And," says Midge, "we're always open to having people with a special skill—like artists or gardeners, for example—come in and share their knowledge with our patients."

SHEPHERD'S ANGELS

Everyone who has followed the story of Shepherd Center knows that the first page could not have been written without the incredible generosity of the hospital's community of donors and volunteers. Nor, indeed, could any of the subsequent pages. The keen desire on the part of the hospital's founders to recognize that generosity took formal shape in 1985 with the inaugural "Angel Luncheon," where, according to Alana Shepherd, "we would officially gather to recognize the efforts of our special volunteers and contributors for the year, and at the same time we would pick one person as the Angel of the Year." The first recipient was Isobel Fraser, who had contributed very generously toward what became the Isobel Fraser Wing for Patient Care on the third floor of the then-new Shepherd Building.

Now under the purview of the Shepherd Center Foundation, the Angel Luncheon is nearing its own silver anniversary. In 2008, at the Piedmont Driving Club, the event honored 112 donors and volunteers and named Bernie Marcus as its Angel of the Year. The special recognition was well deserved, as Mr. Marcus has proven himself one of the hospital's greatest benefactors, whose leadership and gifts have made possible the Billi Marcus Building, the Marcus Community Bridge Program, and the SHARE Initiative.

With deep gratitude we honor again those who have been designated "Angel of the Year":

1985	Isobel A. Fraser*	1998	Dottie Fuqua
1986	Virginia C. Crawford*	1999	Sharon Umphenour
1987	Reunette H. Harris*	2000	Angie Marshall
1988	Carol L. Goodman		Beverly Mitchell
	Helen S. Lanier*	2001	Emory Schwall
1989	Billi Marcus	2002	Lois Puckett
1990	Peggy M. Schwall*	2003	Elizabeth Allen
1991	Sara S. Chapman	2004	Alice Richards*
1992	Anne C. DeBorde*	2005	Ruth D. Anthony
1993	Claire D. Smith	2006	Jennings E. Watkins
1994	Jane Gibson	2007	Paul Brown
1995	Cookie Aftergut		Brian S. (BB) Brown
1996	Marty Church*	2008	Bernie Marcus
	Paul Kennedy*	2009	Gwin A. Oliver
1997	Edna Wardlaw*		Goodloe H. Yancey III

* deceased

Then there are the dozens of "summer volunteers," like the Phoenix Society of Atlanta debutantes and other students whom the hospital might never see again. "But we love them," says Midge. "Patients love their youth and enthusiasm. And those volunteers are getting training and exposure; they're seeing what Shepherd is about, and maybe when they finish their degrees they will come back and work for us."

No surprise, then, that Midge's efforts to increase the numbers of the "independents" has paid off. "It's not hard," she says. "They come to us. They are former patients who want to give back, or friends of our regular volunteers, or people who have read something about Shepherd or seen us in the news. They just need to know the opportunity is here." In fact, says Midge, Shepherd often has more volunteers standing by than the program has work for, which she admits is an unusual—and very fortunate—position to be in. The reason for this, she believes, is that compared to "regular hospitals," the opportunities offered to Shepherd's volunteers are more interesting, more specialized, and, finally, more rewarding.

Working as a volunteer at Shepherd must certainly have some kind of appeal, based on the longevity of service of so many volunteer corps members. "What we like to see, and are seeing more and more," says Midge, "are Junior Committee members graduating into the Auxiliary. Or, best of all, Junior Committee members who, without knowing each other beforehand, ended up marrying, having children, joining the Peach Corps, seeing their children get older, and then themselves moving on into the Auxiliary. We love that progression." Midge describes these veteran volunteers as the heart and soul of the hospital. "As Alana always says, Shepherd was built on donors and volunteers."

Ultimately, Shepherd's volunteers embody Shepherd's spirit—always seeking to do more on behalf of the patients and their families. Midge says that this, too, goes back to Alana, "because she never stops asking what else we can do. And she always has a new idea."

That spirit, undiminished since the hospital's founding, has produced something remarkable, and being part of it, says Midge, has been a wonderful experience. "Imagine—four people had this vision and here we are 35 years later. Starting out with spinal cord injury, expanding to brain injury, MS, and Chronic Pain, and now with initiatives like Beyond Therapy and the Marcus Community Bridge Program, and all the research. It's just fascinating to try to imagine where we will be 10 years from now—to imagine what more we will be able to do."

A Remarkable
Recovery in a
Remarkable Family

*I*n
January 2009, 28-
year-old Chase Anderson suddenly
collapsed from a stroke while running in a race in Miami.
"Nobody could have imagined it," says Shepherd Medical Director Dr. Don
Leslie. "He was an elite runner, in fantastic physical shape." Fortunately, emergency medical personnel were on site at the race, and Chase was rushed to a
nearby hospital on Key Biscayne. He was then transferred to the University
of Miami, where Dr. Dileep Yavagal successfully intervened to break up
the clot in Chase's brain.

Dr. Leslie got the news immediately, thanks to another fortunate
coincidence. He knows Chase personally; in fact, he knows Chase's entire
family, a relationship stretching back 50 years to Dr. Leslie's growing-up
days in Florence, Alabama, where the Anderson clan hails from. Chase's
uncle, Harold Anderson, who lives in Atlanta, is a particularly close
friend, so it's not surprising that Dr. Leslie was quickly in the loop.

Speculating as to what precipitated the stroke, Dr. Leslie explains that Chase had just flown from Hong Kong, where he is an
executive in one of the family businesses, to Miami, where he was
joining the family on vacation. "That's a lot of hours sitting on an air-
plane, and presumably he developed a thrombus, or clot, in his leg during those long hours of immobility. Then, when he got to Miami and got
active again, it embolized—moved up his circulatory system to the heart,
then, in Chase's case, the brain, and caused the stroke."

While Dr. Yavagal's procedure was successful, "Chase still had neurological deficits," says Dr. Leslie. "The report I got was that he had had a serious
stroke and was partially paralyzed on one side." Dr. Leslie and Harold Anderson
immediately flew down to Miami, where Dr. Leslie evalu-
ated Chase and consulted with his
doctors.

Chase in the office of his family's business in Knoxville, TN.

"The result was," he says, "that within just a very few days after the incident we had Chase back here at Shepherd."

Chase remained under Dr. Darryl Kaelin's care as an inpatient at Shepherd for about two months, then continued his recuperation at Shepherd Pathways. "At this point, just over a year later," says Dr. Leslie, "Chase has made an absolutely remarkable recovery. In fact, we actually flew back down to Miami in January 2010, and he ran in the same race that he had run in a year earlier. It's always heartening to see such a wonderful outcome."

The Anderson family has wasted no time showing its appreciation. In late April 2009, shortly after Chase had finished his inpatient stay, he and his mother, Beth, attended the dedication of the Mavis Pruet Leslie Garden (named in honor of Dr. Leslie's mother and created through a gift from Jane Woodruff to adorn the area in front of the George and Irene Woodruff Family Residence Center). "It was a complete surprise to me to see them there," says Dr. Leslie, "and also a wonderful surprise that they took that opportunity to make a donation to Shepherd." That was just the beginning "More recently," says Dr. Leslie, "Chase, Charles Sr. and Hilda [Chase's grandparents], Charles Jr. [Chase's father] and his wife, Molly, and Harold and his wife, Kayrita, hosted us at a luncheon to present the Shepherd Foundation with a major gift."

Yes, the whole family is involved, says Dr. Leslie: "The grandparents, Chase's father and stepmother, his uncle and aunt—not to mention Beth, Chase's mother, and Chase himself. They

Dr. Donald Leslie with Harold Anderson.

have all given back to Shepherd, with incredible generosity."

Dr. Leslie's close friendship with Harold Anderson has also opened another window onto the family's wide-ranging philanthropy. This story began when complications from a knee injury suffered while snow skiing ultimately led—38 operations later—to the amputation of Anderson's leg. "Since that time we've been actively investigating state-of-the-art prosthetics," says Dr. Leslie, "and after the terrible earthquake in Haiti it came to Harold's attention that a huge number of people on the island—the estimate now is more than ten thousand—had immediately become amputees."

As a result, Dr. Leslie, the Harold and Kayrita Family Foundation, and the Hanger Corporation (which manufactured Anderson's prosthetic) have formed a coalition to manufacture prosthetics in Haiti. As of March 2010, Dr. Leslie and Anderson had made five trips to the devastated island. "We're working with the Hospital Albert Schweitzer," says Dr. Leslie. "It's about 50 miles north of Port Au Prince and wasn't damaged in the quake. We've already taken about 30 thousand pounds of equipment down there to get the manufacturing process underway. We're really rolling now; to date 50 Haitians have been fitted with prostheses and are up walking again"

Numerous other examples of the Andersons' good works might be cited, says Dr. Leslie, "because the family is truly remarkable for the way it supports the causes it believes in." And it's fortunate, he adds, that Shepherd Center has become one of those causes.

JANE WOODRUFF

Although the Jane Woodruff Pavilion and the George and Irene Woodruff Family Residence Center (named for Jane's late parents) are relatively recent additions to the Shepherd Center campus, Jane Woodruff has been supporting the hospital since Day One. "Our children grew up together," she says of Alana Shepherd and herself. "I knew James long before his accident, and when that happened, I saw how it transformed Alana's life, how completely dedicated she became to helping other people who were going through what her family had been through." Woodruff calls Alana "the backbone of the hospital," and adds, "I have never seen another woman so tireless, not only at Shepherd but out in the community as well, because that's where all the funding comes from."

Woodruff also enjoys a close relationship with Shepherd's medical director, Dr. Don Leslie, whose mother, Mavis, was a particularly dear friend. The Mavis Pruet Leslie Garden, adorning the area in front of the George and Irene Woodruff Family Residence Center, honors that friendship, as does the fact that the fifth floor of the Jane Woodruff Pavilion was named in Dr. Leslie's honor.

As for having her family's name attached to the new additions, Woodruff generally shuns such recognition and says she agreed to the idea with some reluctance. "It changes things. Your phone doesn't stop ringing, and you get a lot more mail. That's not what I want out of life. I want life to be real and normal." But she admits there's an upside. "I have to say, it's very rewarding when the thanks come back. Of course, you don't do these things for the thanks, but getting those thanks makes you realize how many people you're helping, and in the case of Shepherd, how many people you will continue to help."

BILLI AND BERNIE MARCUS
AND THE MARCUS FOUNDATION

Two of Atlanta's most impactful and influential philanthropists, Billi and Bernie Marcus have supported Shepherd Center since 1984. Over the past 25 years, they have made gifts through the Marcus Foundation, totaling over $18,000,000. Bernie chaired Shepherd Center's "The Best is Yet to Come" capital expansion campaign in 1987, raising $16,000,000 to add space for the Acquired Brain Injury Program; the Outpatient Center, which includes an Aquatic Center, a gym equipped with a full-sized basketball court, a fitness center, and therapy areas; and the Virginia Crawford Research Center, among other facilities—all doubling the size of the hospital in the process. Bernie's lead gift of $500,000 to this campaign provided Shepherd Center's Aquatic Center, which houses an Olympic sized pool used for aquatic therapy, kayaking, competitive swimming and leisure swimming for patients. Bernie later made a second lead gift of over $3,000,000 to give Billi a surprise birthday present, naming The Billi Marcus Building in her honor.

In 1992, Bernie and Billi generously provided a gift of over $1,000,000 to establish the Billi and Bernie Marcus Patient Care Endowment Fund, helping those patients without insurance to receive the care they need. Bernie also served as honorary chairman for Shepherd Center's 25th Anniversary Capital and Endowment Campaign in 2000, helping to raise $64,000,000 to endow Shepherd Center's patient care programs and provide funding that once again doubled the hospital's size—building an expanded cafeteria, new therapy areas and gyms, a family lounge, and a new auditorium. It was Billi and Bernie's gift to this campaign of over $13,000,000 that provided the funding for the Marcus Community Bridge program, which provides patients with post-discharge support for up to one year, helping to bridge the transition from hospital to home, ensuring that the therapies and training learned at Shepherd Center are continued in the patients' home and community. Finally, upon learning in 2008 that many American service personnel who had been injured in Iraq and Afghanistan were not receiving specialized care for traumatic brain and spinal cord injuries, Bernie helped Shepherd Center to forge a partnership with the VA health system and Humana to create the SHARE Initiative, designed to provide specialized rehabilitation at Shepherd Center for wounded veterans. The Marcus Foundation's very generous lead gift of over $2,000,000 challenged the rest of the nation to support our troops by giving to this donor-funded program.

Beyond their philanthropy, both Billi and Bernie have had a deep personal involvement at Shepherd Center. Bernie joined the Advisory Board in 1984, and has served on the Board of Directors since 1987. He was named Shepherd Center's Angel of the Year in 2008. Billi first joined Shepherd Center's Advisory Board in 1995, and has served on Shepherd Center Foundation's Board of Trustees since 2005. She received the Angel of the Year award in 1989, and is a Life Member of Shepherd Center's Auxiliary. In addition, both Billi and Bernie have been longtime supporters of Shepherd Center's annual golf tournament and Legendary Party, and Billi chaired the Shepherd Center Cup (formerly known as The RTM Challenge and The Billi Marcus Classic) for 16 years, from 1987 through 2002.

A Visit With Alana Shepherd

The Shepherd Center tour is over for this morning in the summer of 2009. As she does at least twice a month, Alana Shepherd has led a group of 15 or so visitors on a 90-minute perambulation, pausing to point out a dozen of the hospital's most remarkable features. Among them—

THE GEORGE AND IRENE WOODRUFF FAMILY RESIDENCE CENTER, which provides 30 days of no-fee housing to family members of patients who come from outside the Atlanta area. It's an unbelievable amenity, but Alana explains that having families on campus is a real key to recovery. "Of course it provides comfort and support during the patient's stay at Shepherd, but, just as important, it's an opportunity for family members to become educated as to what their [patient's]care will involve when they get back home. It will help avoid complications."

THE ADOLESCENT PROGRAM, where the injured youngsters go through their therapy sessions, compare notes, and push each other to get better. It's a lively place. The patients have painted their own designs on dozens of the ceiling tiles, and in one corner is a big picture of the adolescent team's "Rockin' and Rollin'" bus. Alana talks about "Operation No Obstacles," where the kids prepare for the challenges of returning to school, and then adds, "Being among your peers is incredibly important in rehab."

THE DAY PROGRAM, on the third floor of the Marcus-Woodruff Building, where patients who have graduated from their inpatient program can continue to improve and get stronger. Here, among other equipment, are the treadmills and the amazing Lokomat machines—high-tech robotic treadmills that allow patients to practice their walking while bearing just as much of their weight as they are capable of. Hanging from one of the machines is a photo of winsome 13-year-old Clara Brown from Maine, who credits the Lokomat with speeding her recovery from an incomplete spinal cord injury she suffered in a gymnastics accident. As Alana says, explaining the tremendous success of the Day Program, "Intense therapy long after injury is the new norm."

THE ASSISTIVE TECHNOLOGY CENTER, also know as "Star Wars"—and always a tour highlight. This is where director John Anschutz and Kevin Grogg show off the latest independence-enhancing wizardry—like the newest innovations in sip-and-puff technology, or voice-activated computers, or word processing programs that somehow transcribe the human voice onto the computer screen, or the incredible "eye-gaze" system, where a camera on the computer responds to signals from the user's eyes. "What they do in here," says Alana, "allows our patients to look into the future and know that things will get better. That's the Shepherd hope."

THE RECREATIONAL THERAPY PROGRAM, on the ground floor of the Marcus-Woodruff Building, whose many components include ProMotion (a fully equipped fitness center for patients and non-patients alike), Livingston Gym (a full-sized basketball court with an indoor track that has banked turns so you don't lose your speed in a racing chair), an art and photography studio, and a 25-yard-long swimming pool featuring wheelchair entry, special water-temperature controls, and, most unique, a deep end. "That's where our patients can get their SCUBA certification," says Alana. "It's the only hospital pool in the country with a deep end." Shepherd patients can participate in an incredible variety of recreational activities, from snow

Alana Shepherd, cofounder of Shepherd Center.

skiing to camping to white-water rafting, not to mention the 11 different team sports that the gym accommodates. Therapeutic recreation was an essential part of founding medical director Dr. David Apple and James Shepherd's vision from Day One, and today the program at Shepherd has 35 to 39 employees. "It's the best in the nation," declares Alana.

Yes, a recurrent motif runs through Alana's tour: Shepherd Center continues to get better so that its patients can continue to get better. That's the mission. So it isn't surprising, when she's asked to recall some of her vivid memories from the early days, that Alana immediately mentions Shepherd's first ventilator patient, who arrived, she guesses, before the first year was done.

"That was impressive," she explains, "because a lot of places wouldn't even take vent patients, so they often got lost out there. Even some of our nurses hadn't seen vent patients in a rehab setting. I think it demonstrated early on that we were serious and that we were capable." Today, adds Alana, Shepherd is one of the very few hospitals in the nation where patients are being weaned off their ventilators using the new diaphragm pacing system (DPS) technology, and that is equally impressive. "These newly injured people are just scared to death when they get here," says Alana, "and something like DPS gives hope: technologies keep improving, outcomes keep getting better."

Of course, other memories well up—not least among them Shepherd Center's move to its own home on Peachtree Road. But the construction of the new facility could only begin, Alana recalls, after a tough fight to have Shepherd's certificate of need (CON) approved by the state. "A review board evaluates these applications," she explains, "and there's no telling who's going to be on that board—everybody from hospital administrators to insurance people and on down the line." Shepherd's application ran into a lot of opposition from people who saw the new hospital as a competitor, a notion Alana dismisses. "We don't compete with anybody in the city," she says, "although we do want their patients who need what we offer, and we wish they wouldn't hold them as long as they do. A few days can make a lot of difference."

One vocal opponent was the hospital that had provided Shepherd's original quarters. "Since we were paying rent, they wanted us to stay," says Alana. "That wasn't going to happen since they were for profit, and the hearings got pretty acrimonious. So much dirty politics gets involved in these things—nasty letters going back and forth, just unbelievable stuff." On the other hand, Shepherd discovered friends it didn't know it had. "One," says Alana, "was a woman representing the public housing sector. She probably didn't know exactly what Shepherd Center was up to or how it would be different from other hospitals, but she voted for us because she had a big heart. She knew that we were going to be trying to help people. We were so elated when things like that happened."

Ultimately the board voted favorably and Shepherd's CON was approved, which led to "the really exciting day when we first brought patients into this building." A special mark of that transition for Alana was seeing the center's mailbox out front. "I thought, 'We are really here. We have our own big blue mailbox. We are now an entity in this city.' That was a really tangible thing. You walked out the door, and there it was."

Alana also recalls with pleasure "when Bernie Marcus started making his first big gifts. We could hardly believe our good fortune." How that all came about is a story she enjoys telling. "Our next-door neighbor at the time, Max Rittenbaum, was a prominent member of Atlanta's Jewish Community. He wanted to help us but wasn't fabulously wealthy himself. So he said, 'I can't give you a lot of money, but I'm going to bring you some people who can.'"

One of those people was Bernie Marcus. "Max brought Bernie over here for a tour," recalls Alana, "and Bernie did give us a nice gift. But then he came back the next year for another visit, which allowed him to see firsthand the difference we were making in people's lives, to really realize what we were doing, and at that point he started making huge gifts." Alana adds that Marcus has always maintained that his gifts to Shepherd have been his best investment "because it was money that gave people back their lives." So that's the story, says Alana: "Max Rittenbaum. He really did come through."

Benefactors like Bernie Marcus and Jane Woodruff lead the list of "wonderful surprises—things we couldn't have anticipated." But much that has happened inside the hosptal has been equally unforeseen, and equally wonderful. "Think of our Andrew C. Carolos MS Center," says Alana, "I never envisioned we would have such a thing, to say nothing of the fact we now have 3,000 people under treatment there." There's also the groundbreaking research now going on at Shepherd.

Generous donations by Mrs. Eula Carlos enabled Shepherd Center to establish
the Andrew C. Carlos Multiple Sclerosis Institute at Shepherd Center as well
as the Eula and Andrew C. Carlos Endowed Chair in MS Research and the
Andrew C. Carlos Endowed MS Research endowment fund.

Alana cites the Geron stem cell research project "that Shepherd is one of the few centers selected to participate in" and the "truly life-changing" DPS procedure available here. "No one could have anticipated these things."

Much of the hospital's ascent, says Alana, can be attributed to Dr. Apple. "He was so great to stretch out like he did, to have such a large vision," she says, and that reminds her of another wonderful surprise. "The quality of the medical people who apply to work here now is unbelievable. Of course, they want to come here because of the programs we have, and then great doctors attract other great doctors. But these people could be working anywhere." Nor does Alana fail to mention Shepherd's nurses and therapists—"many of whom have been here for years, and they are such pros, so good at what they do."

How about unpleasant surprises or unexpected difficulties? Alana doesn't have to mull this question over. "The worst, by far," she says, "was what we went through trying to stage the Paralympic Games in Atlanta." Shepherd was the first sponsor for the games, Alana notes, initially investing $150,000 to secure the bid and to provide office space, supplies and staff, and eventually contributing approximately $750,000. She quotes Harald Hansen, Chairman of the Board of the Atlanta Paralympics Organizing Committee, to the effect that "Without Shepherd Center there would have been no Atlanta Paralympic Games."

But, says Alana, "The Atlanta Committee for the Olympic Games (ACOG) did everything in its power to make things difficult for us. Someone tore all the wires out of stadium when they left, just pulled them out of the ceiling and left them hanging. They trashed the athletes' housing facilities at Georgia Tech. We had two weeks to get everything fixed back up. When the athletes vacated the dorms, ACOG placed buckets in the villages for room key collection, which meant APOC had to rekey all the doors. It made no sense, but they felt like they were competing against us, and they put roadblocks in front of us at every turn. Fortunately, other people came forward to help—because it was the right thing to do."

Still living in ignominy, as far as Alana is concerned, are the major sponsors "who would not support us and would not release their categories either." There were six of them, including McDonald's and Anheuser-Busch "It wouldn't have hurt them at all to say, 'We can't sponsor you, but we'll release the category so somebody else can.' Alana believes that turning away potential sponsors was another of ACOG's tactics to thwart the Paralympics. "I know Duane Ackerman at Bellsouth was told that he didn't need to give any money to the Paralympics because he had already supported the Olympics, but I assured him we needed his support as well. And he did come through for us."

Having to run the obstacle course that ACOG deliberately set up, says Alana, "was incredibly frustrating, disappointing, and really traumatic. On the other hand, to see those games go on—successfully, on time, and on budget—was the most wonderful feeling in the world." And Alana notes that, ultimately, the Paralympics did receive great sponsor support; Coca-Cola and Home Depot led the way, followed soon by UPS and others—"again because it was the right thing to do." U.S. Senator Paul Coverdell and U.S. Representative Newt Gingrich also helped by garnering desperately needed support from the Armed Services. Alana adds that even ACOG eventually came around, contributing $15 million in in-kind support once the Olympic Games were over.

Atlanta's Paralympic Games left a positive legacy, too, because from that year on the Paralympics were brought under the Olympic banner and would never again feel like an abandoned stepchild. Alana gives Olympics czar Juan Antonio Samaranch credit, though his image is not entirely burnished in her memory. "Actually, I wasn't an admirer of his," she says, "and I had good reason."

Alana remembers an occasion when her group was in Switzerland "to pay homage," waiting for the great man to appear in the conference room where they had gathered. During every Olympics over which he presided, it was Samaranch's tradition to ask for two weeks of peace around the world, and his request sometimes had a positive impact. It occurred to Alana that he ought to extend that period of peace to include the weeks of the Paralympics as well. "Think of the lives that might be saved." She told the aide who was in the room with them that she wanted to suggest the idea to Samaranch, and the aide said, "Well, I'll have to ask him if it's OK." The aide left the room, and, then, as Samaranch was about to enter, he reported back to Alana: "No, his Excellency doesn't want you to ask him that question."

"I have never been so angry in my life," says Alana today. "Would it have hurt him to say that? Would it have diminished his stature? No. It would have elevated it. But, no, I was not to put his Excellency on the spot."

As for the positive side of the ledger, however, Alana recalls that in Barcelona, after Atlanta had been awarded the subsequent games, Samaranch sat next to her at one of the venues. "I told him, 'You know, both the Olympics and the Paralympics should be governed by the same committee, by a single committee, rather than by two different committees that end up competing for every single dime.' He said, 'You're right.' And after the Atlanta games, he made that happen."

From her gratitude to those who supported Atlanta's Paralympic Games, Alana turns again to those who have so generously supported Shepherd Center. "John Carlos just gave us a very large gift to buy additional Bioness electrical stimulation equipment," she says. "John is an MS patient who uses a Bioness unit himself, but he's over here enough to see people with no funding for such a device, and he knows that Bioness technology is making a positive difference in the lives of Shepherd patients. Isn't that unbelievable?" In fact, says Alana, of all the wonderful surprises, that might be the most wonderful of all—how somebody always seems to step forward, and you never know who it might be: "Especially now that Shepherd Center's reach is so wide. We just received a tremendous gift from the McCormick Foundation in Chicago. That means so much to us."

What Shepherd Center has achieved in 35 years, what it has evolved into, constitutes an almost unimaginable success story. Who gets the credit? "Well," says Alana, "first of all, James does. Of course, he's the one who suffered for it, but it's more than that. He has really grown into the job of chairman of the board. He got a degree in business administration from the University of Georgia (UGA), and he has developed a tremendous understanding of politics and science, along with hospital administration. The time he might have spent on the tennis court, under other circumstances, he's been in front of the computer, doing research, thinking about issues and problems, reading and digesting tons of material. I admire that. He has really risen to the occa-

Without Shepherd Center there would have been no Atlanta Paralympic Games.

Harald Hansen
CHAIRMAN OF THE BOARD OF
THE ATLANTA PARALYMPICS
ORGANIZING COMMITTEE

sion—and he believes passionately in the hospital." Next—or really in the same breath—comes Dave Apple. "Dave's role has been huge. Not only did he lead the hospital for 30 years, but he has always been so generous with both his time and his money, always willing to go the extra mile, always thinking outside the box, and always available to staff. I really have to give him all the credit in the world."

Will Alana take any credit? "I've raised a lot of money," she laughs, and, actually, she has found that job, too, exciting and rewarding—especially because it has given her the opportunity to get to know so many people who have been part of the fund-raising effort. "One of my real joys has been getting to know the Junior Committee people," she says. "Some of the original members now have their own children on the committee. When these young adults come up to me and say, 'I'm so-and-so, and my parents are so-and-so,' you just want to hug them. It is really special."

Still, Alana concedes that she has done more for Shepherd than raise money. "I suppose it does mean something that I'm here for people who need a sounding board or need somebody to talk to," she says. "The nurses know that they can tell parents or family members who have a problem, 'Well, go see Mrs. Shepherd.'" Moreover, Alana admits that she might have helped foster the open-hearted, patient-first attitude that prevails at Shepherd. "I've always told the staff, if people get upset about something, don't get huffy or defensive. Instead, say, 'I'm so sorry. Please tell me what I can do to make the situation better.' I really think that kind of approach goes a long way, and I think maybe I get some credit for helping create that atmosphere—the philosophy that we will try our best to make you as happy as we can. We are very customer-service oriented around here, no question about it."

We look at everyone as a person, not as somebody who has been hurt or paralyzed, and we will talk to them accordingly. 'What's your name, where do you live, what do you do, what do you like to do, who are your parents?' That is the great spirit here at Shepherd.

Alana Shepherd

Of course, it's not just "customers" who sing Alana's praises. Throughout the hospital there is virtually universal acknowledgment that "Alana's spirit presides here," that, essentially, Shepherd Center is "Alana's hospital." Alana says she won't deny that "that feeling is out there," nor does she mind it. "I'm glad people feel that way. It's nice. It's empowering. It makes you feel good. It makes you feel like you've accomplished something."

At the same time, she wears the mantle lightly, with grace and humor. She laughs in telling the story about a patient from New Hampshire, and about how Dave Moody, a builder in Atlanta, happened to run into this man up there in his hometown. The subject of Shepherd Center came up, and the guy told Moody, "Well, I was treated very well by the staff at Shepherd, but after Mrs. Shepherd came in and met me, they all started coming in and fluffing up my pillows and everything. I really got the attention then." Alana goes on to mention that there's an item on the admitting sheets, in the patient's medical file, that says, FOA— Friend of Alana. "I guess that's to alert the staff," she says. "Of course that's not supposed to make any difference in their care or in the attention they get, but I do think it's hilarious."

Alana will also admit that she has made—and continues to make—one very special contribution. "I am the mother," she says, "and this terrible accident happened to my son. I've been there. So I can empathize, and I can also help assure these families that it is going to get better. Believe me, they need that knowledge. The faces that come through that door are frozen in shock and grief. But our whole staff embraces this philosophy: we will put our arms around these folks and make them feel special. And we will look at every one as a person, not as somebody who has been hurt or paralyzed, and we will talk to them accordingly: 'What's your name, where do you live, what do you do, what do you like to do, who are your parents?' That is the great spirit here at Shepherd, and if I helped foster that, it's because I've been there."

Legacy is a heavy word, but it's hard to imagine an Atlanta institution more closely associated with its founding family. "Well," says Alana, "you can be sure that 35 years ago Harold and James and I were not sitting around the dining room table talking about a 'legacy.' What happened was that we got the kind of opportunity that you just cannot turn your back on." Other families have told her that they would have liked to have created something similarly significant, "and it's generally people who have a lot more money than we did, but the opportunity wasn't there." Given the circumstances, adds Alana, "it wasn't a happy opportunity. But you don't often get the chance to do something of this magnitude, to do something that really makes a difference, so why would you walk away from it?"

Enough. Alana is quick to turn the conversation back to what Shepherd Center does. "What I find more rewarding and gratifying than anything is when the people who need us— whether from far away or from right here in Atlanta—when they come here to Shepherd to get better. These people have to have courage; they have to pull it together before they leave here. And, in most cases, they do. You can see their progress, and the joy they take from it, and it's a wonderful thing to be a part of. It's an unbelievable experience."

Appendix

Shepherd Center Advisory Board

Year in italics indicates first year of membership

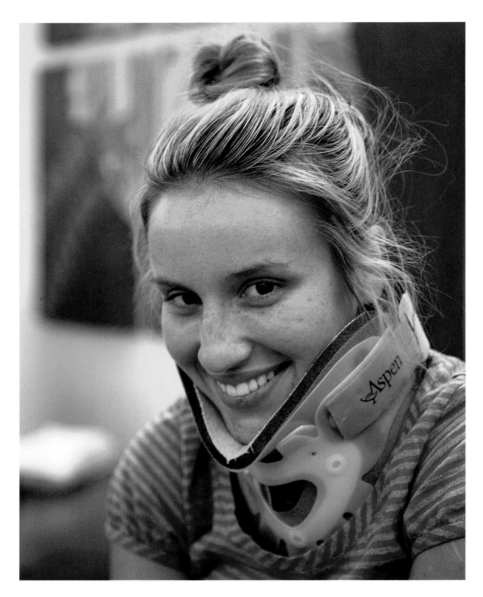

Patient Natalie Shin.

Imagine—
four people had this
vision and here we are 35 years
later. Starting with spinal cord
injury, expanding to brain injury, MS
and Chronic Pain ... It's just fascinating
to try to imagine where we will be 10
years from now—to imagine what
more we will be able to do.

Midge Tracy
Director of
Volunteer Services